Daily Grams™ Student Workbook Grade 5

Daily Grams: Guided Review Aiding Mastery Skills™

Wanda C. Phillips

Easy Grammar Systems™
Post Office Box 25970
Scottsdale, Arizona 85255

www.easygrammar.com

©2002

CAPITALIZATION:

1. is jane's family going to anchorage, alaska, this year?

PUNCTUATION:

2. Tammys dad left at 1 30 in the afternoon

PARTS OF SPEECH: NOUNS

   A noun names a person, a place, a thing, or an idea.
   Circle any nouns:

3. Sharon bought an old sofa for her apartment.

PARTS OF SPEECH: ADVERBS

   Circle any adverbs that tell *when*:

4. We are going today or tomorrow.

ANALOGIES:

   **Analogies show relationships. First, determine how the first two
   words are related. Then, look at the third word and possible
   answers. Choose the answer that has the same relationship to the
   third word.**
   The first two words (set) may be synonyms (have similar meanings).

   Example: Mad is to angry as frequent is to _____.
   (a) always   (b) furious   **(c) often**   (d) infrequent

   Analogies may also be written in this manner:

   Mad : angry :: frequent : _____.
   (a) always   (b) furious   **(c) often**   (d) infrequent

   Circle the correct answer:

5. large : enormous :: calm : _____
   (a) stormy   (b) upset   (c) peaceful   (d) preoccupied

SENTENCE COMBINING:

6. The pot is made of clay.
   The pot is filled with tulips.
   The tulips are yellow.

_____

_____

DAY 2

CAPITALIZATION:

1. in september, mr. and mrs. pino will visit the grand canyon.

PUNCTUATION:

2. That plant is tall leafy and healthy

SUBJECT/VERB:

> **The subject of a sentence tells *who* or *what* the sentence is about. The verb tells what *is (was)* or what *happens (happened)*.**

Note: Prepositional phrases usually aren't the subject or the verb. Deleting them makes finding the subject and verb easier.

Example: Cal was ~~on the phone with his best friend~~.

Underline the subject once and the verb twice:

3. We laughed about the scar on my toe.

SENTENCE TYPES:

> **A declarative sentence makes a statement.**

> **Write a declarative sentence about your shoe:**

4. _____

ANALOGIES:

> **Circle the correct answer:**

5. smart : intelligent :: lives : _____
    (a) dwellings   (b) resides   (c) rural   (d) packs

SENTENCE COMBINING:

6. Kim's aunt is a dentist.
    Kim's aunt lives in Virginia Beach.

    _____

    _____

CAPITALIZATION:

1. last saturday we went to riverside park on cherry lane.

PUNCTUATION:

2. No we cant follow you

PARTS OF SPEECH: PREPOSITIONS

Prepositional phrases begin with a preposition and end with a noun or a pronoun (such as *me, him, her, us,* or *them.*) Commonly used prepositions are *to, for, from, in, into, on,* and *with.*

Circle any prepositional phrases:

3. Come with us.

PARTS OF SPEECH: ADVERBS

Circle any adverbs that tell *how:*

4. They skate fast.

ANALOGIES:

Circle the correct answer:

5. tasty : delicious :: tardy : _____
    (a) late   (b) naughty   (c) bell   (d) tired

SENTENCE COMBINING:

6. Their father is a salesman.
    Their grandfather is a salesman.

    _____

    _____

DAY 4

CAPITALIZATION:

1. is thomas jefferson's home located in virginia?

PUNCTUATION:

2. Their new address is 9400 N Offenhauser Drive Flagstaff Arizona   86004

SUBJECT/VERB:
    Underline the subject; circle the verb that agrees with the subject:

3. Dorita (has, have) a new baby brother.

PARTS OF SPEECH: NOUNS
    A concrete noun names a real thing.   Example: milk
    An abstract nouns names an idea.   Example: truth
    Write C if the noun is concrete; write A if the noun is abstract:

4. A. _____ magnet   B. _____ tower   C. _____ trust

SPELLING:
    A word may end with a single consonant + e. A word ending with consonant + e usually drops that final e when adding a suffix (ending) that begins with a VOWEL. The e is not dropped if the suffix begins with a consonant.
        Examples: time + ing = timing   time + less = timeless
    Write the correct spelling of these words:

5. A.   frame + ed - _____
    B.   price + ing - _____
    C.   price + less - _____

SENTENCE COMBINING:

6. His cousin is on a baseball team.
    His cousin plays third base.

    _____

    _____

CAPITALIZATION:

1. my grandfather's favorite place is wood's canyon lake.

PUNCTUATION:

2. I need the following raisins peanuts and coconut

PARTS OF SPEECH: VERBS
   Write the contraction:

3. A. who is - _____   D. did not - _____

    B. have not - _____   E. I am - _____

    C. we are - _____   F. I have - _____

PARTS OF SPEECH: PRONOUNS
   Circle the correct answer:

4. (Jim and I, Me and Jim, Jim and me) found several deer paths.

SPELLING:
   Write the correct spelling of these words:

5. A. use + ing - _____

    B. use + ful - _____

    C. lease + ed - _____

SENTENCE COMBINING:

6. Maria called to her puppy.
    She held out her arms.

    _____

    _____

DAY 6

CAPITALIZATION:

1. on washington's birthday, i went to newport beach in california.

PUNCTUATION:

2. Dear Anna

    Ill meet you by the fountain

    Pedro

PARTS OF SPEECH: ADVERBS

Circle any adverbs that tell *where*:

3. The mouse scampered here and there.

DICTIONARY SKILLS: ALPHABETIZING

Write these words in alphabetical order:

4. offer   pioneer   noodle   manner   onion   nerve

ANALOGIES:

The first two words of an analogy may be antonyms (opposites). Again, look at your third word; your answer must have an opposite meaning of the third word.

Example: Stay : leave :: quiet : _____.
(a) quite   **(b) noisy**   (c) peacefu   (d) dreams

Circle the correct answer:

5. laugh : cry :: deep : _____
(a) river   (b) depend   (c) shallow   (d) dry

SENTENCE COMBINING:

6. Allie's hair is brown.
Allie's hair has blonde streaks in it.
Allie's hair is curly.

_____

_____

CAPITALIZATION:

1. is pike's peak part of the rocky mountains of the united states?

PUNCTUATION:

2. Taras wedding shower was held on December 31 2000

SYNONYMS/ANTONYMS/HOMONYMS:
Homonyms are words that sound alike but are spelled differently.

Write a homonym for the following words:

3. A. pale - _____   B. seen - _____

PARTS OF SPEECH: NOUNS
A common noun does not name a specific person, place, or thing. *bay*
A proper noun names a specific person, place, or thing. *Hudson Bay*

A *type* is a common noun. A pagoda is a type of building; it is a common noun.

Write **C** if the noun is common; write **P** if the noun is proper:

4. A. ____ horse   B. ____ palomino   C. ____ Breeze (name of a horse)

SPELLING:
A word ending with vowel + consonant + consonant (VCC) usually just adds a suffix. Examples: risk + ed = risk**ed**   bash + ful = bash**ful**

Write the correct spelling of these words:

5. A. post + ed - _____
    B. harm + less - _____
    C. board + ing - _____

SENTENCE COMBINING:

6. Aren is taking his mother to a restaurant.
    It is her favorite restaurant.
    It is her birthday.

_____

_____

DAY 8

CAPITALIZATION:

1. does mr. ernesto lopez work for the eagle express corporation?

PUNCTUATION:

Punctuate this outline:

2. I Snakes
    A Rattlesnakes
    B Cobras
    II Lizards

PARTS OF SPEECH: NOUNS
A common noun does not name a specific person, place, or thing. *dog*
A *type* of a person, place, or thing is still a common noun. *bulldog*
A proper noun names a particular person, place, or thing.
    Examples: common noun - person   common noun - boy
               proper noun - Marco

Write <u>C</u> if the noun is common; write <u>P</u> if the noun is proper:

3. A. ____ MONTH   B. ____ APRIL   C. ____ DAY   D. ____ TUESDAY

PARTS OF SPEECH: VERBS
Circle the correct answer:

4. She (don't, doesn't) know how to do that.

ANALOGIES:
Circle the correct answer:

5. sort : arrange :: block : _____
    (a) build   (b) obstruct   (c) allow   (d) wooden

SENTENCE COMBINING:

6. Magma is molten rock.
    It forms below the earth's surface.

_____

_____

CAPITALIZATION:

1. during the first week of september, matt attended park meadows school.

PUNCTUATION:

2. Capt C L Linski lives in a two story townhouse in Hollywood California

SENTENCE TYPES:
>   **An interrogative sentence asks a question. It expresses a complete thought and ends with a question mark.**
>   **Write an interrogative sentence:**

3. _____

PARTS OF SPEECH: CONJUNCTIONS
>   **Conjunctions are joining words.**
>   **Unscramble these commonly used conjunctions:**

4. A. ro - _____   B. nda - _____   C. btu - _____

ANALOGIES:
>   **The first two words of an analogy may be antonyms (opposites). Then, the third word and the answer must also be opposites.**
>
>   Example: enter : exit :: punish : _____
>   (a) cry   **(b) reward**   (c) discipline   (d) scold
>
>   ***Enter* is the opposite of *exit*; the opposite of *punish* is *reward*.**
>   **Circle the correct answer:**

5. bold : timid :: narrow : _____
    (a) stingy   (b) decrease   (c) limited   (d) broad

SENTENCE COMBINING:

6. Sponges have no tissue.
    Sponges have no organs.

_____

_____

DAY 10

CAPITALIZATION:

1. the rossen house at heritage square is a famous historical building.

PUNCTUATION:
A noun of direct address is used to speak to someone.
If the noun of direct address is the first word, place a comma after it.
   Example: *Marlo*, may I help you?
If the noun of direct address is the last word, place a comma before it.
   Example: May I help you, *Marlo*?
If the noun of direct address is anywhere within the sentence, place a comma before it and a comma after it.
   Example: May I, *Marlo*, go with you?

2. Brian will you make strawberry filled pancakes for breakfast

SENTENCE TYPES:
Write an interrogative sentence:

3. _____

PARTS OF SPEECH: VERBS
A verb may be one word: Example: Tate <u>kicked</u> the ball.
A verb phrase consists of more than one word.
Verb phrase = helping verb(s) + main verb

   Example: Jonah <u>had planned</u> a party for his parents.
Underline the subject once and the verb phrase twice:

4. Several speakers have presented their ideas.

ANALOGIES:
Circle the correct answer:
5. always : never :: partially : _____
   (a) closely   (b) recently   (c) completely   (d) practically

SENTENCE COMBINING:

6. Leeches are worms.
   They have suckers on both ends.

   _____

CAPITALIZATION:

1.   we read about zion national park in our social studies class.

PUNCTUATION:

2.   Im buying a three wheeled bike said Nana

PARTS OF SPEECH: ADJECTIVES
      Many adjectives are descriptive adjectives.
      Write a descriptive adjective; draw an arrow to the word it describes:

3.   A _____ squirrel dashed up the _____ tree.

PARTS OF SPEECH: VERBS
       There are twenty-three helping (auxiliary) verbs.
      Unscramble these nine helping verbs:

4. A. od - _____   D. sha - _____   G. mya - _____
     B. sode - _____   E. veah - _____   H. gimht - _____
     C. ddi - _____   F. adh - _____   I. utsm - _____

SPELLING:
      Write the correct spelling of these words:

5.   A.   digest + ed - _____
      B.   amuse + ing - _____
      C.   brave + ly - _____

SENTENCE COMBINING:

6.   The pie is peach.
      The pie is flaky.
      The pie is moist.

_____

_____

DAY 12

CAPITALIZATION:

1.   i watched a movie entitled <u>the ten commandments</u>.

PUNCTUATION:

2.   Yes hes fifty two years old today

PREFIXES/ROOTS/SUFFIXES:

   re + do + ing = redoing
   prefix   root   suffix

   Five prefixes that are commonly used to express *not:*
   un - **un**happy   **il** - **il**legal   **in** - **in**active
   non - **non**washable   **im** - **im**mature

   Write an appropriate prefix:

3.   A. _____ stop   C. _____ decisive   E. _____ possible
     B. _____ legible   D. _____ kind

PARTS OF SPEECH: PRONOUNS

   A pronoun takes the place of a noun.

        Examples: girl - **she** or **her**   boy - **he** or **him**   car - **it**

   Write a pronoun in each blank:

4.   Carlo and _____ pulled out stools and sat on _____.

ANALOGIES:

   Circle the correct answer:

5.   tell : ask :: defend : _____
     (a) protect   (b) championship   (c) guard   (d) attack

SENTENCE COMBINING:

6.   Jasmin made a dress.
     The dress is pink.
     The dress is flowered.

CAPITALIZATION:

1. for christmas dinner, her mother served new england clam chowder.

PUNCTUATION:

2. Yikes Youre here already

PARTS OF SPEECH: CONJUNCTIONS
Conjunctions are joining words. The three most commonly used conjunctions are *and*, *but*, and *or*. These are called coordinating conjunctions.

Write two appropriate conjunctions:

3. A. Jack _____ his dad will be shopping for groceries.

    B. Jack _____ his dad will be shopping for groceries.

PARTS OF SPEECH: VERBS
<u>May</u> is used to ask permission or to express that someone or something could possibly do something.
        Examples: *May* I go, too?   I *may* go to Canada this summer.

<u>Can</u> means *to be able*.   Example: Mary *can* build sturdy birdhouses.

Circle the correct verb:

4. A. (May, Can) we sleep in a tent on our next camping trip?
    B. (May, Can) you break this in two for me?

SPELLING:

Write the correct spelling of these words:

5. A. vote + ing - _____

    B. pale + ness - _____

SENTENCE COMBINING:

6. Quahana Parker was a great Comanche chief.
    Micah is related to him.

_____

_____

DAY 14

CAPITALIZATION:

1. the first u. s. government was formed under the <u>articles of confederation</u>.

PUNCTUATION:
   Write the abbreviation:

2. A. mountain - _____   B. inch - _____   C. avenue - _____

PARTS OF SPEECH: PREPOSITIONS

   Prepositional phrases begin with a preposition and end with a noun or a pronoun (such as *me, him, her, us,* or *them*). Commonly used prepositions are *to, for, from, in, into, on,* and *with*.

   Circle any prepositional phrases:

3. This note from Mr. Davis is for my mom.

PARTS OF SPEECH: VERBS
   Circle the correct verb:

4. Their mother has (went, gone) to the airport.

ANALOGIES:
   Circle the correct answer:

5. weak : strong :: build : _____
      (a) destroy   (b) contractor   (c) erect   (d) blueprints

SENTENCE COMBINING:

6. The spine protects the spinal cord.
    The spine also forms the backbone of the skeleton.

   _____

   _____

CAPITALIZATION:

1. dear clint,

    dr. vendi, our veterinarian, came to examine our new horse last saturday.

    always,
lulu

PUNCTUATION:

2. Were staying until 5 30 P M on Sunday April 1

PARTS OF SPEECH: ADVERBS
Circle the correct adverb:

3. Holly runs (faster, fastest) than her sister.

PARTS OF SPEECH: VERBS
There are twenty-three helping (auxiliary) verbs.
Unscramble these nine helping verbs:

4. A. dosluh - _____   D. lshal - _____   G. eb - _____
    B. dowlu - _____   E. liwl - _____   H. gebin - _____
    C. doclu - _____   F. nac - _____   I. nebe - _____

SPELLING:
Write the correct spelling of these words:

5. A.   blaze + ed - _____
    B.   rehearse + ing - _____
    C.   trump + et - _____

SENTENCE COMBINING:

6. A rattlesnake has a forked tongue.
    It is a venomous snake.

    _____

    _____

DAY 16

CAPITALIZATION:
   Capitalize a proper adjective but not the noun it modifies.
   Example: **Portugal** (noun)   -   **P**ortuguese (proper adjective)
                     He worked for a **P**ortuguese boat captain for two years.

1.   did betsy ross make the first american flag in boston?

PUNCTUATION:
   Use underlining or quotation marks:

2.   A.   Homeward to America   (title of a book)   B.   Dexter McDwyer   (title of a poem)

PREFIXES/ROOTS/SUFFIXES:
   **A root is a base from which words are formed. Some roots can
   stand alone as a word; some form only a part of a word.**
   ***Therm* is a root that relates to heat.**

   Using this information, explain the word, *thermometer:*

3.   _____

PARTS OF SPEECH: NOUNS
   Circle any nouns:

4.   His brother just bought a van.

SPELLING:
   **A word ending with vowel + vowel + consonant (VVC) usually just adds
   a suffix.**   Examples: reap + ed = reap**ed**   bait + ing = bait**ing**
   Write the correct spelling of these words:

5.   A.   braid + ed - _____   C.   boil + ing - _____
      B.   steam + er - _____   D.   tear + ful - _____

SENTENCE COMBINING:

6.   Plants use sunlight to make their food.
      Plants use water to make their food.
      Plants use carbon dioxide to make their food.

      _____

      _____

CAPITALIZATION:

1. we read about africa's victoria falls last march.

PUNCTUATION:

2. Marta muttered   Your feet are covered with mud

PARTS OF SPEECH: VERBS
Some verbs can serve as either a helping verb or a main verb.
A main verb stands alone.
Example: Jemima <u>does</u> her homework at four o'clock.

A verb phrase consists of helping verb(s) plus a main verb.
Example: Jemima <u>does</u> not <u>like</u> science very much.

Place a √ if the sentence contains a helping verb:

3. A. ____ Carlos <u>did</u> the dishes.   C. ____ I <u>have</u> an old penny.
    B. ____ We <u>did</u> not <u>want</u> advice.   D. ____ <u>Do</u> you <u>have</u> a plastic funnel?

PARTS OF SPEECH: NOUNS
Plural means more than one.
Most plurals are formed by adding s to the noun.
Place a √ if the plural is formed by adding s.

4. A. ____ fist   B. ____ request   C. ____ cry   D. ____ hunch

SPELLING:
One-syllable words ending in consonant + vowel + consonant (CVC)
usually double the final consonant when adding a suffix beginning with
a VOWEL. They usually do not change when adding a suffix beginning
with a consonant.   Examples: trim + ing = trimming   trim + ness = trimness

Write the correct spelling of these words:

5. A. clap + ed - _____   B. drab + ness - _____

SENTENCE COMBINING:

6. The circus is coming to town.
    I cannot attend.

_____

DAY 18

CAPITALIZATION:

1.   last summer, dr. and mrs. j. r. stone went to everglades national park in florida.

PUNCTUATION:

2.   Was the two oclock bus Ms Dunfy on time today

PARTS OF SPEECH: VERBS
     Circle the correct verb:

3.   Please (sit, set) beside me.

WORDS:
     Circle the correct word:

4.   They took their dog on an outing, (too, to, two).

ANALOGIES:
     Circle the correct answer:

5.   car : automobile :: color : _____
     (a) rainbow   (b) crayon   (c) hue   (d) colorless

SENTENCE COMBINING:

6.   Hang gliders use currents of hot, rising air to stay aloft.
     These hot, rising air currents are called thermals.

_____

_____

CAPITALIZATION:

1. did walter cronkite, a famous journalist, work for colonial broadcasting system?

PUNCTUATION:

2. Susan did Mrs Prince arrive for her appointment at 2 30

PARTS OF SPEECH: VERBS
Circle the correct verb:

3. Have you (chose, chosen) the most colorful frame?

PHRASES/CLAUSES:
A phrase is a group of words.   Example: with my aunt
A clause contains a subject and a verb.
Example: While I was eating
Write P if the words form a phrase; write C if the words form a clause:

4.   A. _____ For five minutes   B. _____ When Bo laughs

ANALOGIES:
The first word of an analogy may express a general topic, and the second word may state a type/category of that topic. Choose the answer that has the same relationship to the third word.
Example: Book : mystery :: tree : _____
(a) woods   (b) hiking   **(c) oak**   (d) winter
Circle the correct answer:

5. meal : breakfast :: gem : _____
(a) ruby   (b) precious   (c) jewelry   (d) metal

SENTENCE COMBINING:

6. A solid is a type of matter.
A liquid is a type of matter.
A gas is a type of matter.

_____

_____

DAY 20

CAPITALIZATION:

1. on april fools' day, mayor dougal usually goes to the bahama islands.

PUNCTUATION:
Place a comma between two adjectives that describe unless one adjective is a color or a number.
    Examples: *Bright, shiny* shells were strung on a bracelet.
                Twinkling **red** lights shone in the dark.

2. Long sharp hooks stuck out from Miras fishing lure

PARTS OF SPEECH: ADJECTIVES/ADVERBS
Good **is a describing word (adjective).**   Example: They are good artists.
Well **is an adverb that tells** *how.*   Example: They draw well.

Circle the correct word:

3. Kimo is a (good, well) baker; he makes crescent rolls especially (good, well).

PREFIXES/ROOTS/SUFFIXES:
A root is a base from which words are formed. Some roots can stand alone as a word; some form only a part of a word.

Vis is a root that has to do with sight.

Using this information, explain the word, *vision:*

4. _____

ANALOGIES:
Circle the correct answer:

5. chair : rocker :: boat : _____
    (a) lake   (b) oar   (c) canoe   (d) banks

SENTENCE COMBINING:

6. Ben will give his sister a necklace.
    The necklace is gold.
    The necklace has three pearls.

    _____

    _____

CAPITALIZATION:

1. the aztec indians of mexico were conquered by cortez.

PUNCTUATION:

2. No his name wasnt listed as Romero Roberto

PARTS OF SPEECH: PREPOSITIONS
   A prepositional phrase is a group of words that begins with a preposition. The object of the preposition (O.P.) is the word (noun or pronoun) that ends a prepositional phrase.
   Example: Lolita ran **to her room**.   *Room* is the object of the preposition.
   Circle the prepositional phrase; label the object of the preposition - O.P.:

3. The children were playing in the rain.

PARTS OF SPEECH: NOUNS
   A possessive noun shows ownership.
   If the noun is singular (one), place an apostrophe (') + s to form the possessive.   Example: boots belonging to Todd: Todd**'s** boots

4. A.   a truck belonging to Pat - _____

   B.   a mayor of that town - _____

SPELLING:
   Write the correct spelling of these words:

5. A.   bowl + er - _____

   B.   thin + ed - _____

   C.   sense + less - _____

SENTENCE COMBINING:

6. Supersonic jets can travel faster than the speed of sound.
   This is called Mach 1.

   _____

   _____

DAY 22

CAPITALIZATION:

1. the marzanno family owns an italian restaurant called roma gardens.

PUNCTUATION:
An interrupter is a word or group of words that can be used for emphasis. Example: These apples are, **in fact,** rotten.

An interrupter can add an additional thought.
Example: This orange, **I think,** was grown in Florida.
Use commas to set off interrupters.

2. The weather I believe will be clear today

SYNONYMS/ANTONYMS/HOMONYMS:
Homonyms are words that sound alike but are spelled differently. Synonyms are words with similar meanings.

3. A. Write a homonym for flea: _____

   B. Write a synonym for tug: _____

SUBJECT/VERB:
A compound subject means that there are *two or more* subjects.

Example: My <u>cousin</u> and <u>I</u> play two-square.

Underline the subject once and the verb twice:

4. Her jacket and mittens match.

ANALOGIES:
Circle the correct answer:

5. candy : fudge :: sport : _____
   (a) ball   (b) stadium   (c) athlete   (d) tennis

SENTENCE COMBINING:

6. Jamilla takes acting lessons.
   She wants to become a Broadway actress.

_____

_____

CAPITALIZATION:

1.   a french pilot, louis bleriot, crossed the english channel in a monoplane.

PUNCTUATION:

2.   Stop the car   exclaimed Chan

PARTS OF SPEECH: ADVERBS
   Use *well* to describe how someone is doing (has done) something.
   Circle the correct word:

3.   The baby took his first step last week and is now walking (good, well).

PARTS OF SPEECH: INTERJECTIONS
   Circle the interjection:

4.   Yikes! I nearly lost my balance and fell off the balance beam!

SPELLING:
   Remember:
   Words ending VVC do not usually change when adding any suffix.
         Example: load + ed = loaded
   Words ending VCC do not usually change when adding any suffix.
         Example: bend + ing = bending
   Words ending consonant + e usually drop the e when adding a suffix
   that begins with a vowel. They usually do not drop the e when adding
   a suffix that begins with a consonant. Example: hope + ful = hopeful
   Write the correct spelling of these words:

5.   A.   love + ly - _____

      B.   press + ure - _____

      C.   tour + ing - _____

SENTENCE COMBINING:

6.   The platypus is a mammal.
     It lays eggs.

DAY 24

CAPITALIZATION:

1. last summer, grandpa raced stock cars at paradise speedway in alabama.

PUNCTUATION:

2.

              (A)   16329 Blackmore Lane
                            Henderson NV 89015
                            June 20 20--

    (B)   Dear Miss Sells

FRIENDLY LETTER:
    There are five parts to a friendly letter: heading, closing, signature, salutation (greeting), and body.

    Use the letter in #2 to answer these questions:

3. A. Part A is the: 1) body   2) salutation   3) heading   4) closing
      B. Part B is the: 1) closing 2) salutation   3) signature   4) body

SENTENCE TYPES:
    An imperative sentence gives a command. It expresses a complete thought and ends with a period.

    Place a √ if the sentence is imperative:

4. A. ___   Raise your right hand.
      B. ___   Tate raised his right hand.
      C. ___   Raise your right hand, please.

ANALOGIES:
Circle the correct answer:

5. save : spend :: collect : _____
    (a) tax   (b) distribute   (c) require   (d) cower

SENTENCE COMBINING:

6. The twenty teeth a baby first gets are called primary teeth.
    They are also called milk teeth.

_____

_____

CAPITALIZATION:

1. pisgah national park is in the blue ridge mountains of north carolina.

PUNCTUATION:

2. Bruce Rick and Nathan went to the Y M C A to exercise

SUBJECT/VERB:
>   **The subject of a sentence tells *who* or *what* the sentence is about.**
>   **The verb tells what *is (was)* or what *happens (happened)*.**

Note: Prepositional phrases usually aren't subject or verb. Deleting them makes finding the subject and verb easier.
>   Example: Janell <u>ran</u> ~~with her brother~~.

Underline the subject once and the verb or verb phrase twice:

3. During the summer, Logan worked at a dude ranch.

PARTS OF SPEECH: NOUNS
>   **Plural means more than one.**
>   **Words ending in *s, sh, ch, x,* and *z* add <u>es</u> to form the plural.**

4. A. A word that ends in *sh* is _____; its plural is _____.

    B. A word that ends in *x* is _____; its plural is _____.

    C. A word that ends in *s* is _____; its plural is _____.

ANALOGIES:

Circle the correct answer:

5. migrate : move :: moisten : _____
    (a) dampen   (b) moisture   (c) dried   (d) fasten

SENTENCE COMBINING:

6. Kami's mother is an author.
    She writes children's books.

DAY 26

CAPITALIZATION:

1. william l. shoemaker, a successful jockey, won four kentucky derbies.

PUNCTUATION:

2. Outing List
    -bandages
    -bottled water
    -toothbrush

PARTS OF SPEECH: VERBS
Some verbs can serve as either a helping verb or a main verb.
        Example: Garth **had** a cavity.   (main verb)

A verb phrase consists of helping verb(s) plus a main verb.
        Example: Garth **had gone** to his dentist.   (helping verb)

Place a √ if the sentence contains a helping verb:

3. A. ____   Faith <u>has</u> a rash on her hand.   C. ____   The soup <u>is</u> <u>simmering</u>.
    B. ____   Our mirror <u>has</u> <u>cracked</u> again.   D. ____   Kim <u>is</u> two years old.

PARTS OF SPEECH: ADVERBS
    Circle any adverbs that tell *where*:
4. The banker set her papers aside and looked up.

SPELLING:
    Write the correct spelling of these words:

5. A.   scare + ed - _____
    B.   fresh + ly - _____
    C.   repair + ing - _____

SENTENCE COMBINING:

6. Her brother joined the U. S. Marine Corps.
    He is stationed at Camp Pendleton.

    _____

    _____

CAPITALIZATION:

1. the band from daltson high school marched at a columbus day parade.

PUNCTUATION:

2. The Rev D G Raineri visited patients at St Marys Hospital at 6 P M

PARTS OF SPEECH: VERBS

> **The present tense tells what *is* or what *is happening* now.**
>> Example: Bill <u>collects</u> marbles.

> **The past tense tells <u>past time.</u>**
>> Example: Someone <u>collected</u> the papers.

> **Write <u>PR</u> if the tense is present; write <u>PT</u> if the tense is past:**

3. _____   The child and her father <u>blew</u> bubbles from a jar.

PARTS OF SPEECH: ADJECTIVES

> **Write a describing adjective;   draw an arrow to the noun it describes:**

4. Many _____ rugs were on the _____ floor.

SPELLING:

> **Write the correct spelling of these words:**

5. A.   fashion + able - _____

    B.   release + ing - _____

    C.   press + ed - _____

SENTENCE COMBINING:

6. A butterwort is a plant.
    It traps insects with the sap on its leaves.

_____

_____

DAY 28

CAPITALIZATION:

1. on thanksgiving, miss bengall and i ate at cobbler's inn.

PUNCTUATION:

2. The pilot studied her flight plan checked her watch and boarded the plane

PARTS OF SPEECH: PRONOUNS
> **A pronoun takes the place of a noun.**
> **I, he, she, we, they, you, and it can serve as the subject of a sentence.**

Write a pronoun in each blank:

3. My friend and _____ like math; _____ really enjoy(s) measuring angles.

PARTS OF SPEECH: ADJECTIVES
Circle the correct adjective:

4. My left shoe seems (tighter, tightest) than my right one.

ANALOGIES:
Circle the correct answer:

5. forgiving : unforgiving :: lazy : _____
    (a) idle   (b) lazier   (c) industrious   (d) sluggish

SENTENCE COMBINING:

6. Pia lives on Rainbow Avenue.
    She lives in an apartment complex.
    Tim lives in the same apartments.

    _____

    _____

CAPITALIZATION:

Capitalize these titles:

1. A. <u>sequoia scout</u>   B. <u>cannons of the comstock</u>   C. <u>the key to zion</u>

PUNCTUATION:

2. Their business address is 2193 Cold Creek Drive Sandpoint ID 83864

PREFIXES/ROOTS/SUFFIXES:

Prefixes help to understand word meaning. Some prefixes are used to express numbers.   uni, mono - 1 (**uni**cycle); (**mono**rail)
bi, du - 2 (**bi**lateral); (**du**al)
tri - 3 (**tri**city)

Write an appropriate prefix:

3. A. Yancy's new _____cycle has two huge red wheels.

    B. The toddler rode a three-wheeled vehicle, a _____cycle.

    C. The _____cycle, a one-wheeled vehicle, was hard for me to ride.

    D. When only one person speaks, it is called a _____logue.

PARTS OF SPEECH: NOUNS

Write C if the noun is common; write P if the noun is proper:

Remember: A *type* of a person, place, or thing is still a common noun.

4. A. ____ DAY   B. ____ FRIDAY   C. ____ HOLIDAY

ANALOGIES:

Circle the correct answer:

5. bear : polar :: bridge : _____
   (a) building   (b) suspension   (c) water   (d) ship

SENTENCE COMBINING:

6. Robins live in a nest.
   The nest is located at the top of that maple tree.

   _____

   _____

DAY 30

CAPITALIZATION:

1. her uncle from canada speaks english and french.

PUNCTUATION:
   Use underlining or quotation marks:

2. A. Air Bud   (title of a movie)
    B. It's Feeding Time   (title of a newspaper article)

PARTS OF SPEECH: VERBS
   **The present tense tells what *is* or what *is happening* <u>now</u>.
   The past tense tells *what has already happened*.**

   Write <u>PR</u> if the tense is present; write <u>PT</u> if the tense is past:

3. A. _____   Marco <u>goes</u> to nearly every art show.
    B. _____   Paula <u>delivered</u> several boxes to her mother's office.

PARTS OF SPEECH: PRONOUNS
   Circle the correct usage:

4. (Me and my friend, My friend and I, My friend and me) are ready to help.

ANALOGIES:
   Circle the correct answer:

5. parsley : herb :: manatee : _____
    (a) mammal   (b) dolphin   (c) otter   (d) ocean

SENTENCE COMBINING:

6. A small galaxy may contain about 100,000 stars.
    A large galaxy may contain 3,000 billion stars.

   _____

   _____

CAPITALIZATION:

1. at cost club, i was given a coupon for parchy* crackers.

*brand name

PUNCTUATION:

2. Dear Alicia
    My family and I left for Mexico City on Friday January 19 2001

           Love
           Toni

PARTS OF SPEECH: ADVERBS
Circle any adverbs that tell *how or when:*

3. They often watch the news together.

PARTS OF SPEECH: NOUNS
Some nouns do not change when forming the plural. sheep - sheep

4. An example of a noun that does not change is _____.

ANALOGIES:
Analogies may have a relationship of *part to whole.*
  Finger : hand :: handle : _____
  (a) wagon (b) knob   (c) open   (d) lever

Finger is part of a hand. The third word is *handle*. *Handle* must be a part of an item. Therefore, the answer is *wagon*. A *handle* is part of a *wagon*.

Circle the correct answer:

5. hoof : horse :: claw : _____
    (a) cat (b) talon (c) sharp (d) animal

SENTENCE COMBINING:
6. Each body cell has fluid material.
    This fluid material is called cytoplasm.

    _____

    _____

DAY 32

CAPITALIZATION:

1. did aunt susan attend a community meeting held at friendship bible church?

PUNCTUATION:

2. The boys bathroom is locked said Jacy

PARTS OF SPEECH: VERBS
   Write the contraction:

3. A. he is - _____   D. you are - _____
    B. we will - _____   E. they have - _____
    C. were not - _____   F. I shall - _____

SENTENCES/FRAGMENTS/RUN-ONS:
   Write <u>S</u> if the words form a sentence; write <u>F</u> for fragment if the words do not form a sentence:

4. A. _____ Many in the middle of the afternoon.
    B. _____ Many campers set up tents in the middle of the afternoon.

ANALOGIES:
   Circle the correct answer:

5. heel : foot :: sole : _____
    (a) soul   (b) shoe   (c) toe   (d) leg

SENTENCE COMBINING:

6. The cupboard is pine.
    The cupboard is three-cornered.
    The cupboard has glass doors.

    _____

    _____

CAPITALIZATION:

1. many pioneers crossed the mississippi river at st. louis, missouri.

PUNCTUATION:

2. Gov Thon and her husband visited Hartford Connecticutt

PARTS OF SPEECH: VERBS
A regular verb adds _ed_ to the past and past participle.

	past	**past participle**
Example: to wave	wav**ed**	(had) wav**ed**

An irregular verb changes to form the past and past participle.
Example: to sing   **sang**   (had) **sung**

Place a √ if the verb is regular:

3. A. ___ to lean   C. ___ to praise   E. ___ to swim
    B. ___ to fly   D. ___ to rise   F. ___ to make

DICTIONARY SKILLS: ALPHABETIZING
Alphabetize these words:

4. grab   core   great   easy   heart   crime

ANALOGIES:
Circle the correct answer:

5. sleeve : coat :: anchor : _____
    (a) ship   (b) metal   (c) weight   (d) movement

SENTENCE COMBINING:

6. Her favorite food is chicken.
    She likes it marinated in mustard sauce.

_____

_____

DAY 34

CAPITALIZATION:

1. jay is attending the schooner days and blues festival in rockland, maine.

PUNCTUATION:

2. No I dont want milk juice or soda

PARTS OF SPEECH: PREPOSITIONS
        A prepositional phrase is a group of words that begins with a preposition. The object of the preposition is the word (noun or pronoun) that ends a prepositional phrase.
                Examples: from his **mother**   with **us**
        Circle the prepositional phrase; label the object of the preposition - <u>O.P.</u>:

3. This gift is for Lani.

PARTS OF SPEECH: NOUNS
        A concrete noun names a real thing.
        An abstract noun names an idea.

        Write <u>C</u> if the noun is concrete; write <u>A</u> if the noun is abstract:

4. A. _____ faith   B. _____ protection   C. _____ fort

ANALOGIES:
    Circle the correct answer:

5. act : play :: stanza : _____
        (a) meter   (b) lines   (c) story   (d) poem

SENTENCE COMBINING:

6. Maria hit the softball.
    Maria ran to first base.
    Maria waved her hands excitedly.

    _____

    _____

CAPITALIZATION:

1. lida yelled, "don't touch that south african mamba!"

PUNCTUATION:

2. Toby do I add one half cup of cream to this dessert

SENTENCE TYPES:

An exclamatory sentence shows excitement or some other strong emotion. It expresses a complete thought and ends with an exclamation point.

Place a √ if the sentence is exclamatory:

3. A. ___ I can do it!
   B. ___ Yikes! I left my money in the bathroom!
   C. ___ She is a terrific hockey player.

PARTS OF SPEECH: ADVERBS

Circle the correct adverb:

4. She pressed (harder, hardest) on the third lever.

ANALOGIES:

The first two words of an analogy may express whole to part. Then, the answer must express a part of the third item.

Example: watermelon : slice :: boot : _____
(a) shoe   **(b) heel**   (c) leather   (d) work

Circle the correct answer:

5. team : player :: herd : _____
   (a) ranch   (b) round-up   (c) steer   (d) clan

SENTENCE COMBINING:

6. This oven cleaner is effective.
   This cleaner is poisonous.

   _____

   _____

DAY 36

CAPITALIZATION:

1. dear nikko,

    i'll be leaving in the morning. thanks for everything.

    your friend,

    ricky

PUNCTUATION:

2. Well whos the companys new vice president

SUBJECT/VERB:

Compound means more than one.

Underline the compound subject once and the verb or verb phrase twice:

3. Scissors and tape fell from her hands.

PARTS OF SPEECH: ADJECTIVES/ADVERBS

Write *good* or *well*:

4. This is a _____ story; you write _____.

ANALOGIES:

Circle the correct answer:

5. shoe : foot :: glove : _____
    (a) hand   (b) mitten   (c) winter   (d) clothing

SENTENCE COMBINING:

6. It has rained for two days.
    Edroe Street is flooded.

    _____

    _____

CAPITALIZATION:

1. the qin dynasty in china reigned from 255-206 b. c.

PUNCTUATION:
   Punctuate this outline:

2. I Flowers
      A Bulbs
         1 Daffodils
         2 Tulips
      B Seedlings
   II Shrubs

PARTS OF SPEECH: **ADVERBS/ADJECTIVES**
   Circle the correct word:

3. Ellie kicked that ball (good, well).

SUBJECT/VERB:
   A compound verb means that there are *two or more* verbs.

   Underline the subject once and the verb twice:

4. Shannon raised her hand and waved.

SPELLING:
   **A one-syllable word ending with consonant + vowel + consonant
   (CVC) will usually double the final consonant when adding a suffix
   beginning with a VOWEL. It will not double the final consonant
   when adding a suffix beginning with a consonant.**
      Examples: ship + ing = shipping   ship + ment = shipment

   Write the correct spelling of these words:

5. A. beg + ing - _____   C. scar + ed - _____

   B. but + er - _____   D. cap + tion - _____

SENTENCE COMBINING:

6. Luke bought groceries.
   Before that, he went to the bank.

   _____

   _____

DAY 38

CAPITALIZATION:

1. does st. basil's cathedral in russia have an onion-shaped dome?

PUNCTUATION:

2. Pictures of a writers conference appeared in a two page layout

PREFIXES/ROOTS/SUFFIXES:

A suffix is an ending; it is added to a root.
Ward or wards are suffixes that mean in a given direction.
Using this information, explain the word, westward:

3. _____

SUBJECT/VERB:

Underline the subject; circle the verb that agrees with the subject:

4. After the ice storm, the roads (was, were) very dangerous.

SPELLING:

Write the correct spelling of these words:

5. A. insure + ance - _____

    B. drop + ed - _____

    C. trust + ing - _____

SENTENCE COMBINING:

6. These pants need to be ironed.
    These pants are wrinkled.

_____

_____

CAPITALIZATION:

1.   in history class, molly and ryan studied about the incas of peru.

PUNCTUATION:

An appositive is a noun or noun phrase (more than one word) that is placed beside another noun to explain it. Use commas before and after an appositive.

Example: Mt. Fuji, **a mountain in Japan,** is beautiful.

2.   Sparky our new dog is our familys first pet

PARTS OF SPEECH: NOUNS

Circle any nouns:

3.   Bob and his sister went to a beach in Texas.

PARTS OF SPEECH: VERBS

Circle the correct verb:

4.   A.   They had (rode, ridden) their horses into a canyon.

    B.   Her aunt must have (flown, flew) to Wyoming on business.

    C.   That contractor should have (builded, built) his house closer to the road.

ANALOGIES:

Circle the correct answer:

5.   flashy : showy :: fidgety : _____
    (a) sensitive   (b) inactive   (c) hibernate   (d) restless

SENTENCE COMBINING:

6.   Jana's watercolor won a prize.
    It was of a parrot.
    She was very happy.

_____

_____

DAY 40

CAPITALIZATION:

1. the himalaya mountains in asia extend for thousands of miles.

PUNCTUATION:

   Write the abbreviation:

2. A. building - _____   B. pint - _____   C. teaspoon - _____

PREFIXES/ROOTS/SUFFIXES:

   A root is a base from which words are formed.
   ***Script* is a root that relates to writing.**

   Using this information, explain the word, *inscription*:

3. _____

PARTS OF SPEECH: ADJECTIVES/ADVERBS

   ***Good* is a describing word (adjective).**   Example: They are good artists.
   ***Well* is an adverb that tells how.**   Example: They draw well.

   When stating a person's health, use *well*. Example: I don't feel well.

   Circle the correct word:

4. A. Lars is a (good, well) plumber.

   B. After having a tetanus shot, Penny didn't feel (good, well).

ANALOGIES:

   Circle the correct answer:

5. captured : released :: common : _____
   (a) normal   (b) extraordinary   (c) plain   (d) familiar

SENTENCE COMBINING:

6. The world's largest desert is the Sahara.
   It covers nearly one-third of Africa.

   _____

   _____

CAPITALIZATION:

Capitalize this outline:

1. i. clocks
    a. mainspring
    b. pendulum
    ii. watches

PUNCTUATION:

2. Hes twenty one and a diver from Bangor Maine

PARTS OF SPEECH: VERBS

Circle the correct verb:

3. You (may, can) go with us if you want.

WORDS:

Their shows ownership.	Example: *Their* cat is a Persian.
There shows place.	Example: Go *there* in the morning.
They're is a contraction for they are.	Example: *They're* next in line.

Circle the correct word:

4. A. He sat (there, they're, their) in silence.
    B. (There, They're, Their) planning a surprise for (there, they're, their) sister.

ANALOGIES:

Circle the correct answer:

5. cards : birthday :: games : _____
    (a) activities   (b) fun   (c) board   (d) events

SENTENCE COMBINING:

6. James Naismith created the game of basketball.
    He did this for the Y. M. C. A.
    The year was 1891.

_____

_____

DAY 42

CAPITALIZATION:

1. the battle of yorktown ended the american revolution.

PUNCTUATION:

2. Kenny asked Wheres my red baseball cap

PARTS OF SPEECH: CONJUNCTIONS
   Circle any coordinating conjunctions:

3. Dakota and his brother will attend the play, but they'll buy tickets at the door.

FRIENDLY LETTERS/ENVELOPES:

4. _____

   Tara Hill
   222 North 81st Street
   Scottsdale, AZ   85267

                              Noah Liston
                              4937 East Oak Street
                              Gettysburg, PA   17325

   _____

   A.   Who is sending this letter? _____
   B.   What is on the third line of the return address?_____

ANALOGIES:
   Circle the correct answer:

5. movement : motion :: scent : _____
   (a) aroma   (b) scenic   (c) delivered   (d) flowers

SENTENCE COMBINING:

6. The boy emailed his friends.
   The boy then went to meet his friends.

   _____

   _____

CAPITALIZATION:

1. susan asked, "did a british man build a steam locomotive called the <u>rocket</u>?"

PUNCTUATION:

> **An interrupter is a word or group of words that can be used for emphasis.**   Example: His dad**, obviously,** likes to sail.

> **An interrupter can add an additional thought.**
> Example: My aunt**, as a matter of fact,** owns this restaurant.
> **Use commas to set off interrupters.**

2. This beef jerky without a doubt is the toughest Ive ever eaten

PARTS OF SPEECH: PRONOUNS
> **A pronoun takes the place of a noun.**
> *Me, him, her, us, them, you,* **and** *it* **can serve as an object of a sentence.**

Write an appropriate pronoun:

3. The coach told Mona and _____ to go into the game.

WORDS:

Circle the correct word:

4. A. (Their, There, They're) ad has not appeared in the newspaper.

> B. Would you like to travel (there, their, they're)?

> C. They want (too, to, two) pack early.

> D. (May, Can) you lift this bucket of water?

ANALOGIES:

Circle the correct answer:

5. empty : vacant :: pretty : _____
    (a) beckoning   (b) attractive   (c) entering   (d) hollow

SENTENCE COMBINING:

6. His aunt is visiting from Detroit.
    She is only staying for two days.

_____

_____

DAY 44

CAPITALIZATION:

1. my uncle darius lives near the savannah river in the south.

PUNCTUATION:

2. Dear Mr and Mrs Bencze   **(A)**

    Yes youre invited to visit us in Santiago Chile   **(B)**

                        Respectfully   **(C)**
                        Ria   **(D)**

FRIENDLY LETTER:
   There are five parts to a friendly letter: heading, closing, signature, greeting (salutation), and body.
   Write the parts of the letter shown in #2:

3. A. _____   C. _____

    B. _____   D. _____

PARTS OF SPEECH: NOUNS
   Write the plural ending:

4. A. wax____   B. prong____   C. lens____   D. rich____

ANALOGIES:
   Some analogies show the relationship of an item and its use.
   Choose an answer that has the same relationship to the third word.
   Example: iron : press :: toothbrush : _____
              (a) teeth   **(b) clean**   (c) sleep   (d) gums
   Circle the correct answer:

5. saw : cut :: ladle : _____
    (a) pierce   (b) scoop   (c) spread   (d) fork

SENTENCE COMBINING:

6. Lake Baikal is in Russia.
    It is the world's largest freshwater lake.

    _____

    _____

CAPITALIZATION:

1. did dad study the chinese language at a college in the east?

PUNCTUATION:

2. Sasha lifted her long well toned arm to shoot the basketball

SENTENCES/FRAGMENTS/RUN-ONS:

Write S if the words form a sentence; write F for fragment if the words do not form a sentence:

3. A. _____ Hal hit the nail squarely on the head.
    B. _____ During the afternoon, roamed through the woods.

SUBJECT/VERB:

Underline the subject once and the verb or verb phrase twice:

4. The rabbi and his son visited a homeless shelter.

ANALOGIES:

Circle the correct answer:

5. mixer : combine :: lasso : _____
    (a) chase   (b) rodeo   (c) hemp   (d) catch

SENTENCE COMBINING:

6. These pears are juicy.
    These pears are ripe.
    These pears are large.

_____

_____

DAY 46

CAPITALIZATION:

1. during the middle ages, castles were built in england.

PUNCTUATION:

2. Whoa This ski lift is so high exclaimed Miss Dee

SUBJECT/VERB:

Underline the subject once and the verb or verb phrase twice:

3. Their suitcases toppled from the conveyor belt at the airport.

DICTIONARY SKILLS: GUIDE WORDS

Two words appear in boldfaced type at the top of each dictionary page. These are called guide words. The first word listed is the first word (entry) on that page. The second word listed is the last word (entry) on that page.
Example: dangerous - dim

Place a √ if the word will appear on a page with the guide words:

badge - beside:

4. A. ___ band   B. ___ brain   C. ___ back   D. ___ berth

ANALOGIES:

Circle the correct answer:

5. limousine : transport :: umbrella : _____
    (a) rain   (b) carry   (c) protect   (d) flourish

SENTENCE COMBINING:

6. Mr. Hart became perturbed.
    Mr. Hart received another incorrect bill.

_____

_____

CAPITALIZATION:

1. his aunt belongs to the frequent traveler club sponsored by atlantic airlines.

PUNCTUATION:

2. Lena said   My uncle lives in Naco Mexico

SYNONYMS/ANTONYMS/HOMONYMS:
Homonyms are words that sound alike but are spelled differently.
Synonyms are words that have similar meanings.
Antonyms are words with opposite meanings.

Write <u>H</u> if the words are homonyms, <u>S</u> if the words are synonyms, and <u>A</u> if the words are antonyms:

3. A. ____ love - detest   B. ____ doctor - physican   C. ____ gait - gate

PARTS OF SPEECH: NOUNS
A common noun does not name a specific person, place, or thing.
A proper noun names a specific person, place, or thing.
A *type* is a common noun.

4. A. Write a common noun: _____

    B. Write a proper noun: _____

ANALOGIES:

Circle the correct answer:

5. peeler : pare :: yardstick : _____
    (a) ruler   (b) measure   (c) distance   (d) feet

SENTENCE COMBINING:

6. The raft is square.
    The raft is large.
    It is slightly deflated.

_____

_____

DAY 48

CAPITALIZATION:

1. a hispanic festival was held near fairmont parkway last friday.

PUNCTUATION:
   Place commas before and after a title that follows a name within a sentence.   Example: Mona Hu, D.O., is their physician.

2. Sal Rice R N works at St Johns Hospital in Jackson Mississippi

PREFIXES/ROOTS/SUFFIXES:
   The prefixes, *pre* and *fore*, are commonly used to express *before:*
               pre - pre plan   fore - fore tell
   Write an appropriate prefix:

3. A. _____heat   B. _____wash   C. _____warn   D. _____told

PHRASES/CLAUSES:
   A phrase is a group of words.   Example: beyond that goal post
   A clause contains a subject and a verb.   Example: When <u>you</u> <u>smile</u>
   Write P if the words form a phrase; write C if the words form a clause:

4. A. _____ Except a few shrimpers   B. _____ After we wrote our stories

ANALOGIES:
   Sometimes, the first two words will be nouns but still reflect "used by."
            Example: Bow : archer :: vase : _____
                      (a) flowers   (b) urn   (c) water   **(d) florist**
            A *bow* is used by an *archer*; a *vase* is used by a *florist*.
   Circle the correct answer:

5. clay : potter :: wood : _____
    (a) tree   (b) forest   (c) carver   (d) mayor

SENTENCE COMBINING:

6. The monkey is swinging.
    The monkey is making funny faces.

_____

_____

CAPITALIZATION:

1. has mayor miller spoken at the rotary club?

PUNCTUATION:

2. Jay asked   Whos Lisas teacher

PARTS OF SPEECH: ADJECTIVES

> **When a linking verb such as *to taste, to smell,* or *to look* is used in a sentence and *was or were* can replace it, use <u>good</u>, not *well.***
>
> were
>
> Example: The seaweed cookies <u>**tasted**</u> good.

> **Replace the linking verb with *was* or *were*;   circle the correct word:**

3. The freshly baked bread smelled (good, well).

PREFIXES/ROOTS/SUFFIXES:

> **A suffix is an ending; it is added to a root.**
> **Ly is a suffix that can mean *happening again at specific times.***

> **Using this information, explain the word, *weekly*.**

4. _____

SPELLING:

> **Write the correct spelling of these words:**

5. A.   map + ing - _____
    B.   relish + ed - _____
    C.   refine + ment - _____

SENTENCE COMBINING:

6. We planted daisies in our flower garden.
    We planted petunias in our flower garden.
    We planted daffodils in our flower garden.

    _____

    _____

DAY 50

CAPITALIZATION:

Capitalize the name of a political party.

Example: Does she belong to the **R**epublican **P**arty?

1. is the democratic party meeting at uncle don's house?

PUNCTUATION:

2. The baby took a bite of food smiled and spit it out

PARTS OF SPEECH: ADVERBS

Circle the correct word:

3. Don't talk so (loud, loudly).

PARTS OF SPEECH: VERBS

Some verbs can serve as either a helping verb or a main verb.
Write <u>HV</u> if the boldfaced verb is a helping verb; write <u>MV</u> if the boldfaced verb is a main verb:

4. A. ____ These nails **are** rusty.   C. ____ I **was** told the truth.
    B. ____ These pots **are** made of clay.   D. ____ I **was** not at home.

SPELLING:

Write the correct spelling of these words:

5. A. slurp + ing - _____
    B. capture + ed - _____
    C. swim + ing - _____

SENTENCE COMBINING:

6. Most butterflies fly by day.
   Most moths fly by night.

_____

_____

CAPITALIZATION:

1.   the butcher's shop is south of pebble shoe company on royal street.

PUNCTUATION:
>   **An appositive is a noun or noun phrase that explains another word beside it. Use a comma before an appositive if it ends a sentence.**
>   Example: Please hand this to my mother, **the woman in the pink suit.**

2.   This package is for Tate R Trainer the towns only doctor

PARTS OF SPEECH: ADJECTIVES
>   **Circle any adjective that describes:**

3.   She pulled a small, woolen hat over her black curly hair.

SUBJECT/VERB:
>   **Underline the subject once and the verb twice:**

4.   Several people in the park stopped and watched the playful puppies.

SPELLING:
>   **Remember:**   **A word ending in vowel + consonant + _e_ usually drops the _e_ when adding a suffix beginning with a vowel. A word ending in vowel + consonant + _e_ usually does not drop the _e_ when adding a suffix beginning with a consonant.**
>   Examples: time + ing = timing
>   time + ly = timely

>   **Write the correct spelling of these words:**

5.   A.   late + ly - _____

      B.   line + ing - _____

      C.   skim + er - _____

SENTENCE COMBINING:

6.   A camel is a ruminant.
      A ruminant chews its cud.

_____

_____

DAY 52

CAPITALIZATION:

1.   is rockefeller center near lincoln tunnel in manhattan, new york?

PUNCTUATION:

2.   Take me with you   Kendra demanded

PARTS OF SPEECH: ADVERBS
   Circle any adverbs that tell *where, when,* or *how:*

3.   Ian said restlessly, "Let's go somewhere later."

PARTS OF SPEECH: VERBS
   Write the contraction:

4.   A.   he is - _____   D.   you are - _____
   B.   we will - _____   E.   they have - _____
   C.   were not - _____   F.   I shall - _____

ANALOGIES:
   Circle the correct answer:

5.   famed : well-known :: concealed : _____
   (a) sealed   (b) hidden   (c) weapon   (d) open

SENTENCE COMBINING:

6.   Jason and Hope ran five miles.
   They were tired.

   _____

   _____

CAPITALIZATION:

1. have you been to bow lake in southeastern new hampshire?

PUNCTUATION:

2. Boat Rules   Do not go beyond chained area
                    Hold on while moving around

PARTS OF SPEECH: PRONOUNS
   If <u>we</u> or <u>us</u> stands beside a noun, cross out the noun and choose the correct pronoun.
      Example: Please stay with (we, us) friends during the football game.
                 Please stay with (we, **us**) ~~friends~~ during the football game.

   Circle the correct pronoun:

3. (We, Us) teammates have to decide.

PARTS OF SPEECH: ADJECTIVES/ADVERBS
   Circle the correct word:
4. Janet and Brian draw animals (good, well).

ANALOGIES:
   Circle the correct answer:

5. noisy : quiet :: fragile : _____
    (a) sturdy   (b) delicate   (c) glass   (d) breakable

SENTENCE COMBINING:

6. Christina's sister is a waitress.
    Christina's sister works at a Mexican food restaurant.

    _____

    _____

DAY 54

CAPITALIZATION:

1. did john adams help to ratify the declaration of independence?

PUNCTUATION:

2. Ill need the following snacks   crackers apples and sunflower seeds

PARTS OF SPEECH: PRONOUNS
  Circle the correct pronoun:

3. Please let (we, us) girls look through your telescope.

PARTS OF SPEECH: ADJECTIVES
  When a linking verb such as *to taste, to smell,* or *to look* is used in a sentence and *was or were* can replace it, use good, not well.

was

Example: The hot chocolate smelled good.

  Replace the linking verb with *was* or *were*; circle the correct word:

4. That sticky bun looks (good, well).

ANALOGIES:
  Circle the correct answer:

5. ugly : attractive :: trusting : _____
   (a) trust   (b) suspicious   (c) sneaky   (d) deliberate

SENTENCE COMBINING:

6. Lance was happy with his grades.
   Lance threw his report card into the air.

   _____

   _____

CAPITALIZATION:

1. the members of the new haven german club planted trees on labor day.

PUNCTUATION:
   Use underlining or quotation marks:

2. A. Beautiful Brown Eyes (title of a song)   B. Town Tribune (name of a newspaper)

PARTS OF SPEECH: VERBS
   Present tense tells what *is* or what *is happening* <u>now</u>.
      Example: I <u>want</u> a hot dog.
   Past tense tells <u>past time</u>.   Example: Jen <u>blew</u> glass in her studio.
   Future tense tells something that <u>will happen</u>.
      Example: It <u>will snow</u> in the mountains today.
   Write <u>PR</u> if the tense is present, write <u>PT</u> if the tense is past, and write <u>FT</u> if the tense is future.

3. A. _____   The book show <u>lasted</u> four hours.
    B. _____   My grandmother <u>will ski</u> with us.
    C. _____   Barry <u>cooks</u> in his spare time.

PARTS OF SPEECH: NOUNS
   Write <u>C</u> if the noun is common; write <u>P</u> if the noun is proper:

4. A. ____ CHRISTMAS   B. ____ CELEBRATION   C. ____ PARADE

ANALOGIES:
   Circle the correct answer:

5. rely : depend :: observe : _____
    (a) find   (b) serve   (c) claim   (d) see

SENTENCE COMBINING:

6. Chandra lifted the garbage lid.
    Chandra saw a snake.
    Chandra screamed.

_____

_____

DAY 56

CAPITALIZATION:

Capitalize the name of a government body.

Example: The **U. S. C**ongress must approve all treaties.

1.   the u. s. house of representatives meets today.

PUNCTUATION:

2.   Please take this to the teachers workroom said Miss Krupa

PHRASES/CLAUSES:

A phrase is a group of words.
Example: across the bridge

A clause contains a subject and a verb.
Examples: This <u>topping is</u> fat free.
When <u>he was</u> ten years old

Write <u>P</u> if the words form a phrase; write <u>C</u> if the words form a clause:

3.   A. _____   Cheering loudly for their team.
     B. _____   Your umbrella is in the closet.

PARTS OF SPEECH: ADJECTIVES
Circle the correct adjective:

4.   These enchiladas become (hotter, hottest) when heated a second time.

ANALOGIES:
Circle the correct answer:

5.   relay : race :: penny : _____
     (a) nickel   (b) Lincoln   (c) pound   (d) coin

SENTENCE COMBINING:

6.   Juan is rather quiet.
     His brother is loud and boisterous.

_____

_____

CAPITALIZATION:

1. take constitution avenue to be near to the lincoln memorial in washington, d. c.

PUNCTUATION:

2. Is the girls club located at 909 W Van Riper Road Montvale NJ   07645

SENTENCE TYPES:

The four sentence types are declarative, interrogative, imperative, and exclamatory.

Write the sentence type:

3. A. _____ Bach was a famous composer.
    B. _____ Have you seen the Tower of London?
    C. _____ Don't tickle me.

PARTS OF SPEECH: NOUNS

Nouns ending in *ff* usually add *s.*   muff - muffs

Nouns ending in *f* may add *s*; however, some change the *f* to *v* and add *es.*   leaf - leaves   Consult a dictionary if you are uncertain.

Place a √ if the noun adds s:

4. A. ___ puff   B. ___ loaf   C. ___ whiff   D. ___ chief

SPELLING:

Write the correct spelling of these words:

5. A. amaze + ment - _____
    B. rude + ly - _____
    C. compose + ing - _____

SENTENCE COMBINING:

6. Most volcanoes lie in a zone called "Ring of Fire."
    This is near the edge of the Pacific Ocean.

_____

_____

DAY 58

CAPITALIZATION:

1. in reading class, we discussed "sea fever" by john masefield.

PUNCTUATION:

2. This pantry we believe needs to be stocked with the following soup rice and tuna

CLAUSES:
>   **All clauses contain a SUBJECT and a VERB.**
>   **An independent clause expresses a complete thought and can stand alone.**   Example: <u>We</u> <u>sat</u> on the pier for an hour.
>   **A dependent clause does not express a complete thought.**
>   Example: After the basketball <u>team</u> <u>ran</u> onto the court
>   **Write <u>IC</u> if the clause is independent; write <u>DC</u> if the clause is dependent:**

3. A. _____   Where we could see a hole in the fence.

    B. _____   It rains frequently in Princeville in January.

PARTS OF SPEECH: ADVERBS
   Circle the correct adverb:

4. His twin bowls (better, best) than he.

SPELLING:
   Write the correct spelling of these words:

5. A. present + er - _____

    B. meet + ing - _____

    C. debate + or - _____

SENTENCE COMBINING:

6. Erosion can be caused by water.
    Erosion can be caused by wind.
    Erosion can be caused by ice.

CAPITALIZATION:

Capitalize the first two lines of the poem, "Birches":

1. when i see birches bend left to right
   across the line of straighter darker trees

PUNCTUATION:

2. Tonys sister lives at 2 Southwest 5th Street Miami FL   33135

PREFIXES/ROOTS/SUFFIXES:

A root is a base from which words are formed. Some roots can stand alone as a word; some form only a part of a word.

Port **is from the Latin word,** *portare,* **which means to bear or carry.**

Using this information, explain the word, *transport:*

3. _____

SUBJECT/VERB:

Underline the subject once and the verb or verb phrase twice:

4. A vegetable tray and a carrot cake have been ordered for the party.

ANALOGIES:

Circle the correct answer:

5. newspaper : classifieds :: wheel : _____
   (a) round   (b) spoke   (c) convertible   (d) jeep

SENTENCE COMBINING:

6. Mother is trying to light the grill.
   The charcoal won't ignite.

   _____

   _____

DAY 60

CAPITALIZATION:

1. "is gypsum cave near nelles air force base?" asked kyla.

PUNCTUATION:

2. Mrs Orwigs name was listed on the commencement list as Orwig Lali

FRIENDLY LETTER ENVELOPES:

3. _____

   Tami Begay
   10 Modesto Way
   Shippensburg, PA   17257

                              Julian Vargas
                              920 Deer Crossing Drive
                              Flagstaff, AZ   86101

   _____

   A. What is the zip code of the person sending this letter? _____
   B. What is the last name of the person receiving this letter? _____

PARTS OF SPEECH:
   Circle the correct word:

4. He (don't, doesn't) like to go to the zoo.

ANALOGIES:
   Circle the correct answer:

5. pen : writing :: hammer : _____
   (a) claw   (b) tool   (c) pounding   (d) carpenter

SENTENCE COMBINING:

6. Linda wants to go to Alaska.
   She wants to go with her friends.
   She wants to go this summer.

   _____

   _____

CAPITALIZATION:

1.   did grandpa go aboard the <u>u. s. s. constitution</u> docked in boston?

PUNCTUATION:

2.   12235 Pleasant Street
                                       Salem MA 01970
                                       January 27 20--
         Dear Cal
              Our new rug has an unusual design and is woven
                                       Your uncle
                                       Rafe

FRIENDLY LETTERS:
   Use the letter in #2 to answer these questions:

3.   A.   What part of a friendly letter is *Dear Cal*? _____

     B.   What part of a friendly letter is *Your uncle*? _____

DICTIONARY SKILLS: ALPHATBETIZING
   Write these words in alphabetical order:

4. jade   bath   jar   forest   jail   bass   earn

SIMPLE/COMPOUND/COMPLEX SENTENCES:
   A simple sentence has a subject and a verb.

         Example: <u>He</u> <u>peeled</u> potatoes for dinner.

   **A simple sentence may have a compound subject or a
   compound verb.**
         Example: <u>He</u> and his <u>grandfather</u> <u>peeled</u> potatoes for dinner.

   Write a simple sentence:

5.   _____

SENTENCE COMBINING:

6.   Joy went to the pharmacy.
     Her prescription was not ready.

     _____

     _____

DAY 62

CAPITALIZATION:

1. salton sea is near california's chocolate mountains.

PUNCTUATION:

2. Mario asked Wheres Parkers picture

PARTS OF SPEECH: ADJECTIVES/ADVERBS
Real **is usually an adjective meaning true, sincere, or genuine.**
Really **is an adverb that tells** *to what extent.*
Circle the correct word:

3. A. Poppa gave us a (real, really) gold coin.

    B. I am (real, really) tired.

PARTS OF SPEECH: VERBS
Circle the correct verb:

4. A. She must have (given, gave) us the wrong address.

    B. A jar of salsa had (fell, fallen) from the pantry shelf.

SPELLING:
A word ending in consonant + y usually changes the y to i before adding a suffix beginning with a vowel. However, many words do not drop the y when adding ing.
Examples: try + ed = tried   try + ing = trying
Write the correct spelling of these words:

5. A. study + ed - _____

    B. study + ing - _____

    C. study + s - _____

SENTENCE COMBINING:

6. Eyeballs are protected by bony structures.
    These bony structures are called orbits.

    _____

    _____

CAPITALIZATION:
   Capitalize this outline:

1.   i.   mineral resources

   a.   oil

   b.   coal

   ii.   other resources

PUNCTUATION:

2.   Jana asked Arent your parents from Finland Kami

PARTS OF SPEECH: VERBS
   Write a √ if the verb is regular:

3.   A. _____ to stop   B. _____ to pour   C. _____ to bring   D. _____ to try

PARTS OF SPEECH: PRONOUNS
   A pronoun takes the place of a noun.
   Me him, her, us, them, you, whom, **and** *it* **can serve as an object.**

   Write an appropriate pronoun:

4.   Do you want to go with _____?

SPELLING:
   Write the correct spelling of these words:

5.   A.   rely + ed - _____

   B.   rely + ing - _____

   C.   fry + ing - _____

SENTENCE COMBINING:

6.   The toddler is screaming.
   The child does not want to take a nap.
   His mother is ignoring him.

   _____

   _____

DAY 64

CAPITALIZATION:

Capitalize this heading and greeting of a friendly letter:

1.   12 north perry drive
                                          fort worth, tx   76133
                                          november 3, 20--

    dear anne,

PUNCTUATION:

2.   Yes my mother or my aunt will present a slide show on Tuesday Feb 12

PARTS OF SPEECH: NOUNS

Write C if the noun is concrete; write A if the noun is abstract:

3.   A. _____ staple   B. _____ kindness   C. _____ respect

SENTENCES/FRAGMENTS/RUN-ONS:

Write S if the words form a sentence; write F for fragment if the words do not form a sentence:

4.   A. _____ The creek spilled over its banks.

     B. _____ The fuse box in the garage.

ANALOGIES:

Circle the correct answer:

5.   forget : remember :: strict : _____
     (a) forceful   (b) apparent   (c) lenient   (d) disciplined

SENTENCE COMBINING:

6.   Mark wore a tie.
     It was a pink tie.
     It was a silk tie.
     He wore it with a black suit.
     He was attending his cousin's wedding.

_____

_____

CAPITALIZATION:
Capitalize these titles:

1. A.   <u>the fence post</u>

    B.   <u>colorado history for kids</u>

    C.   "she walks in beauty"

PUNCTUATION:
Punctuate this outline:

2. I Snakes
       A Rattlesnakes
       B Cobras
    II Lizards

PARTS OF SPEECH: ADVERBS
Some adverbs tell *to what extent*. Seven adverbs often tell *to what extent: not, so, very, too, quite, rather, and somewhat.* There are others such as *extremely* and *really.*

Write an adverb that tells *to what extent*:

3. The wind blew _____ briskly through the canyon.

PARTS OF SPEECH: NOUNS
Write the possessive:

4. a pet belonging to that family: _____

ANALOGIES:
Circle the correct answer:

5. trimester : three :: quadruplet : _____
    (a) two   (b) ten   (c) four   (d) six

SENTENCE COMBINING:

6. This stuffed giraffe is musical.
    This giraffe is yellow.
    This giraffe belongs to a baby.

    _____

    _____

DAY 66

CAPITALIZATION:

1. "the african people love their land," said professor shand.

PUNCTUATION:

2. Yes Allen were leaving for Hyattsville at two oclock this afternoon

PARTS OF SPEECH: NOUNS
Plural means more than one.

Place a √ if the noun adds _es_ to form the plural:

3. A. ___ birch   D. ___ shell   G. ___ fizz
   B. ___ splash   E. ___ loss   H. ___ charm
   C. ___ fix   F. ___ mess   I. ___ Christmas

SUBJECT/VERB:
Underline the subject; circle the verb that agrees with the subject:

4. Our team (is, are) in the finals.

ANALOGIES:
Circle the correct answer:

5. response : answer :: banner : _____
   (a) computer   (b) advertising   (c) pennant   (d) teasing

SENTENCE COMBINING:

6. Lightning struck the tree.
   The tree split at its base.

_____

_____

CAPITALIZATION:

1. did king henry VIII of england have a warship named the <u>mary rose</u>?

PUNCTUATION:

2. Jordans family rode on an outrigger a type of canoe used on the ocean

PREFIXES/ROOTS/SUFFIXES:

Prefixes help to understand word meaning:

sub - under (**sub**zero)   **pro - forward** (**pro**cession)
re - again (**re**model); **back**wards (**re**treat)   **hyper - overly** (**hyper**active)

Write an appropriate prefix:

3. A. Our bean sprout is _____merged in water.

   B. She put the car in _____verse.

   C. My skin is _____sensitive.

   D. You may _____ceed.

PARTS OF SPEECH: NOUNS

Circle any nouns:

4. The floats in the parade were displayed in a park near a large statue.

ANALOGIES:

Circle the correct answer:

5. costly : inexpensive :: fake : _____
   (a) rare   (b) false   (c) authentic   (d) fur

SENTENCE COMBINING:

6. Maria's mother likes opera.
   Maria's father does not like opera.

DAY 68

CAPITALIZATION:

Capitalize these lines of poetry by Robert Frost:

1. the rain to the wind said,

    "you push and i'll pelt."

PUNCTUATION:

2. Yes Id love a strawberry filled ice cream cone   declared Mona

PARTS OF SPEECH: VERBS

Circle the correct verb:

3. A. The newspaper is (lying, laying) in the driveway.

    B. Ellen has (boughten, bought) a motorcycle.

    C. Michael had (shook, shaken) his head in protest.

WORDS:

Circle the correct word:

4. A. (May, Can) you drive a car with standard transmission?

    B. I know that (they're, there, their) not hungry yet.

    C. The (to, two, too) year old wants a snack, (to, two, too).

ANALOGIES:

Circle the correct answer:

5. tourist : traveler :: wanderer : _____
   (a) hunter   (b) nomad   (c) gatherer   (d) immigrant

SENTENCE COMBINING:

6. The girl was surprised.
   She placed her hand over her mouth.
   She also giggled.

_____

_____

CAPITALIZATION:

1. we went to galveston, texas, on the gulf of mexico.

PUNCTUATION:
> **Place a comma after <u>two</u> prepositional phrases that begin a sentence.**
>> Example: *With the help of two friends*, we were able to load our van.
> **Place a comma after one <u>long</u> prepositional phrase that begins a sentence.** Example: *After the very disturbing news*, everyone grew quiet.

2. After the babys christening the family gathered at the sister in laws home for lunch

PARTS OF SPEECH: CONJUNCTIONS
> **Write a sentence containing a coordinating conjunction:**

3. _____

PARTS OF SPEECH: ADVERBS
> **Circle any adverbs that tell *how:***

4. Dakota worked quickly but carefully.

SIMPLE/COMPOUND/COMPLEX SENTENCES:
> **A complex sentence may have one complete thought (independent clause) and one or more incomplete thoughts (dependent clauses).**
>> Example: Before <u>we went</u> to the lake, <u>we packed</u> a lunch.
>>> **dependent clause   independent clause**
> **Finish each complex sentence.**

5.   A.   <u>When I was five years old,</u> _____

    B.   <u>After we watched a movie,</u> _____

SENTENCE COMBINING:

6.   Venus is the second planet from the sun.
    Venus is a rocky planet.

_____

_____

DAY 70

CAPITALIZATION:

    Capitalize this outline:

1. i. types of apartments

        a. furnished

        b. unfurnished

   ii. types of houses

PUNCTUATION:

    Write the abbreviation:

2. A. United States - _____   B. meter - _____   C. quart - _____

PARTS OF SPEECH: PRONOUNS
    Circle the correct pronoun:

3. The small child planned to startle Toby and (she, her) by jumping out at them.

PHRASES/CLAUSES:

    A phrase is a group of words.   Example: under the pillow
    A clause contains a subject and a verb.
          Example: If Mr. Haines leaves early

    Write P if the words form a phrase; write C if the words form a clause:

4. A. _____   After you finish your homework

    B. _____   After the second quarter

ANALOGIES:

    Circle the correct answer:

5. flock : sheep :: pack : _____
    (a) travel   (b) luggage   (c) wolf   (d) ram

SENTENCE COMBINING:

6. A small blue jay hopped around the patio.
    The blue jay had a twig in its beak.

_____

_____

CAPITALIZATION:

1.   let's go to woodbury mall near chippenham parkway in richmond.

PUNCTUATION:

2.   The winner by the way hasnt been decided Noah

CLAUSES:

> **All clauses contain a SUBJECT and a VERB.**
> **An independent clause expresses a complete thought and can stand alone.**   Example: My <u>foot was caught</u> between the sofa and a chair.
> **A dependent clause does not express a complete thought.**
> Example: Before <u>I begin</u> my homework

Write IC if the clause is independent; write DC if the clause is dependent:

3.   A. _____   Moses created a ceramic dish.

     B. _____   If you enter by the back door.

PARTS OF SPEECH: VERBS

Circle the correct verb:

4.   One of the boys (speak, speaks) French.

ANALOGIES:

Circle the correct answer:

5.   Salt Lake City : Utah :: Santa Fe : _____
     (a) Phoenix   (b) Mexico   (c) Southwest   (d) New Mexico

SENTENCE COMBINING:

6.   Jina's head hurts.
     She bumped her head on the car door.

     _____

     _____

DAY 72

CAPITALIZATION:

1. is jones bay near croatan national forest in north carolina?

PUNCTUATION:

2. Their grandparents anniversary I assume is next Wednesday July 7

PARTS OF SPEECH: ADVERBS
    Unscramble these adverbs that tell *to what extent:*

3. A. nto - _____   E. ahrter - _____

    B. os - _____   F. wsoaemht -_____

    C. oot - _____   G. iuteq -_____

    D. yevr - _____

SUBJECTS/VERBS:
    In an imperative sentence, the subject is often not stated. It is
    understood to be *you*.
        Example: Sit here.   (You) Sit here.
    Underline the subject once and the verb twice:

4. Wait for me.

ANALOGIES:
    The first two words of an analogy may express a male - female (or
    female - male) relationship. The third word and the answer must show
    the same relationship.   Example: Hen : rooster :: doe :_____
                                       (a) fawn   **(b) buck**   (c) habitat   (d) Bambi

    Circle the correct answer:

5. mare : stallion :: ewe : _____
    (a) sheep   (b) lamb   (c) wool   (d) ram

SENTENCE COMBINING:

6. They drove on Interstate 70 for ten miles.
    Then, they took a county road to a cabin.

    _____

    _____

CAPITALIZATION:

1. yesterday, beth's friend, who lives in the southwest, broke out with german measles.

PUNCTUATION:

Place a dash (the width of M) or parentheses ( ) to provide additional information.

Example: Mora scrubbed walls — very dirty ones.

Mora scrubbed walls (very dirty ones).

2. He did it purposely   to prove a point

DICTIONARY SKILLS: GUIDE WORDS

Two guide words appear in boldfaced type at the top of each dictionary page. The first word listed is the first entry on that page. The second word is the last entry on that page.

Place a √ if the word will appear on a page with the guide words:

tourist - turn:

3. A. ___ towel   B. ___ train   C. ___ tune   D. ___ tool

PARTS OF SPEECH: VERBS

Underline the subject once and the verb or verb phrase twice:

4. During the ice storm, the police and road crews helped stranded motorists.

ANALOGIES:

Circle the correct answer:

5. poet : poetess :: actor : _____
    (a) drama   (b) actress   (c) television   (d) cinema

SENTENCE COMBINING:

6. American football is played with eleven players.
    Canadian football is played with twelve players.

DAY 74

CAPITALIZATION:

1.   governor brinwood, a republican, spoke at a gooseberry inn luncheon.

PUNCTUATION:

2.   Their new son I think is being dedicated on Sunday April 30

SUBJECT/VERB:
   Underline the subject once and the verb twice:

3.   The child took his mother's hand and crossed the lane.

PARTS OF SPEECH: ADJECTIVES/ADVERBS
   Circle the correct word:

4.   Hot cinnamon rolls taste (good, well) early in the morning.

SPELLING:
   A word ending in consonant + y usually changes y to i when adding a suffix beginning with a consonant.   Example: happy + ness = happiness
   Write the correct spelling of these words:

5.   A.   lazy + ness - _____
     B.   merry + ment - _____
     C.   icy + ly - _____

SENTENCE COMBINING:

6.   Treasure maps were handed out.
     The children began to search.
     They were looking for a metal box.

     _____

     _____

CAPITALIZATION:

1. a polynesian lady served us hawaiian chicken at luau restaurant.

PUNCTUATION:

2. Angelo exclaimed   Wow   What a view

PARTS OF SPEECH: VERBS
   Write the contraction:

3. A.   does not - _____   D.   will not - _____
    B.   there is - _____   E.   I have - _____
    C.   they are - _____   F.   should not - _____

PARTS OF SPEECH: ADJECTIVES/ADVERBS
   Circle the correct word:

4. This tape doesn't stick (good, well).

SPELLING:
   **Remember: A word ending in consonant + y usually changes y to i
                when adding a suffix except when adding the suffix ing.**
                Examples: fry + ed = fried   fry + ing = frying
   Write the correct spelling of these words:

5. A.   comply + ance - _____
    B.   steady + ly - _____
    C.   cry + ing - _____

SENTENCE COMBINING:

6. Jim used his new metal detector.
    He found a soda can.
    He found several coins.
    He found a child's shovel.

    _____

    _____

DAY 76

CAPITALIZATION:

1. during the space age, neil armstrong walked on the moon.

PUNCTUATION:
Place a comma before a title if it ends a sentence.
Example: Their professor is Kammie Rivera, Ph.D.

2. Both of his sisters employer is Noah B Troon D D S

PARTS OF SPEECH: ADJECTIVES
Circle any descriptive adjectives:

3. Plush, musical bears were displayed on their soft, leather sofa.

SYNONYMS/ANTONYMS/HOMONYMS:
Homonyms are words that sound alike but are spelled differently.
Synonyms are words that have similar meanings.
Antonyms are words with opposite meanings.

Write H if the words are homonyms, S if the words are synonyms, and A if the words are antonyms:

4. A. ____ pare - trim   B. ____ pare - pair   C. ____ pare - increase

ANALOGIES:
Circle the correct answer:

5. infinite : endless :: dissimilar : _____
    (a) similar   (b) unlike   (c) difficult   (d) finite

SENTENCE COMBINING:

6. His skin is very fair.
    He burns easily.

_____

_____

CAPITALIZATION:

1. the town of wales, alaska, is on the bering strait.

PUNCTUATION:
   Use underlining or quotation marks:

2. A. Boating   (title of a magazine)
    B. Healthy Eating Habits   (title of a magazine article)
    C. Other Skies   (name of a book)

PARTS OF SPEECH: VERBS

   Place a √ if the sentence contains a verb phrase (helping verb):

   **Hint: You may want to delete any prepositional phrases, underline the
              subject once and the verb or verb phrase twice.**

3. A. ____ They are going to Alaska.
    B. ____ These moccasins are unusual.

PREFIXES/ROOTS/SUFFIXES:
   ***Tion* is a suffix that means action or process.**

   Using this information, explain the word, *completion*:

4. _____

SPELLING:
   **Words that end in vowel + y usually do not change when adding a
      suffix.   Examples: pray + ed = prayed   key + ed = keyed**
   Write the correct spelling of these words:

5. A. destroy + ing - _____
    B. pay + ment - _____
    C. replay + ed - _____

SENTENCE COMBINING:

6. The grandmother bathed the baby.
    The grandmother laughed at the baby's silly faces.

   _____

   _____

DAY 78

CAPITALIZATION:

1. did michelangelo, an artist, do a marble sculpture called <u>the rebel slave</u>?

PUNCTUATION:

Place a comma after <u>two</u> prepositional phrases that begin a sentence.
Example: *Before the beginning of the game,* the team warmed up.
Place a comma after one <u>long</u> prepositional phrase that begins a sentence. Example: *From that highest mountain,* we can see the ocean.

2. At the end of the month Julies mom always balances her checkbook

PARTS OF SPEECH: VERBS

Write <u>PR</u> if the tense is *present*, write <u>PT</u> if the tense is *past*, and write <u>FT</u> if the tense is *future*.

3. A. _____ The tram will arrive in ten minutes.

   B. _____ They send humorous cards to their parents.

   C. _____ The phone rang for five minutes.

PARTS OF SPEECH: ADJECTIVES

Circle the correct adjective:

4. Of the various antique dishes, this cake plate, I think, is (older, oldest).

SPELLING:

Write the correct spelling of these words:

5. A. obey + ed - _____

   B. silly + ness - _____

   C. boy + ish - _____

SENTENCE COMBINING:

6. Patty's eyes are large.
   Patty's eyes are blue.
   Patty's eyes are very expressive.

   _____

   _____

CAPITALIZATION:

Capitalize this friendly letter:

1.
                                    921 banyan trail
                                    boca raton, fl 33431   **(A)**
                                    october 12, 20--

    dear aunt sharon,   **(B)**

      have you researched the old coin that we found?   **(C)**

                                    your nephew,   **(D)**
                                    mike   **(E)**

PUNCTUATION:

2. David cant go with us because his brother in law is visiting from Dayton Ohio

FRIENDLY LETTER:
Label the parts of the above friendly letter:

3. A. _____   D. _____
    B. _____   E. _____
    C. _____

PARTS OF SPEECH: PREPOSITIONS
Cross out any prepositional phrases; underline the subject once and the verb or verb phrase twice:

4. On a very clear night, we looked at the moon through our telescope.

SPELLING:
Write the correct spelling of these words:

5. A. response + ive - _____

    B. lace + y - _____

    C. pretty + ly - _____

SENTENCE COMBINING:

6. Tara volunteers several hours a week.
    Tara is a candy striper at a local hospital.

_____

_____

DAY 80

CAPITALIZATION:

1. is the islamic religion also referred to as moslem?

PUNCTUATION:

2. Dear Jemima
   You asked about Nick and Annes wedding They
   were married on Sunday December 24 2000
                        Trena

PARTS OF SPEECH: NOUNS

Write <u>C</u> if the noun is common; write <u>P</u> if the noun is proper:

3. A. _____ GAME   B. _____ CHESS   C. _____ OLYMPICS

PARTS OF SPEECH: PREPOSITIONS

Circle any prepositional phrases; box any object of the preposition:

4. His glasses are on the table by the front door.

ANALOGIES:

The first two words may express cause and effect. The first word states the cause; the second states the result or effect. Therefore, the third word must express a cause; the answer must reflect the result or effect of that.

Example: Decay : cavity :: rain : _____.
              (a) water   (b) chilliness   (c) drizzle   **(d) dampness**

Decay causes a *cavity* in teeth; *rain* causes *dampness*.

Circle the correct answer:

5. laceration : pain :: fire : _____
   (a) heat   (b) fuel   (c) ignite   (d) camping

SENTENCE COMBINING:

6. The trireme was a type of ship used in 400 A. D.
   It was powered by 170 oarsmen.

_____

_____

CAPITALIZATION:

1. the explorer, magellan, rounded cape horn at the tip of south america.

PUNCTUATION:
  If part of a sentence occurs after a city and state, place a comma also after the state.
  Example: Did you ever go to Shreveport, Louisiana, with your parents?

2. Ive always wanted to go to Kansas City Missouri to see my cousins

PARTS OF SPEECH: ADVERBS
  Circle any adverbs that tell *to what extent:*

3. Although the child seems rather ill, her fever is not very high.

PARTS OF SPEECH: VERBS
  Write the contraction:

4. A. you will - _____   D. what is - _____
  B. I would - _____   E. I am - _____
  C. were not - _____   F. you are - _____

ANALOGIES:
  Circle the correct answer:

5. game : enjoyment :: tornado : _____
  (a) pressure   (b) cyclone   (c) destruction   (d) hurricane

SENTENCE COMBINING:

6. The wind blew strongly.
  Waves smashed against the rocks.

  _____

  _____

DAY 82

CAPITALIZATION:
Capitalize these titles:

1. A. <u>ultimate visual dictionary</u>
   B. "in the early morning"
   C. "autos and their owners"

PUNCTUATION:

2. Prepared for the worst Mona marched into her supervisors office

PARTS OF SPEECH: PRONOUNS
Possessive pronouns show ownership.
Possessive pronouns are:	my, mine	our, ours	it, its
	his	their, theirs	
	her, hers	your, yours	

Write an appropriate possessive pronoun:
3. Jana went hiking with _____ dog.

SENTENCE TYPES:
Write the sentence type:

4. A. _____ This is hot!
   B. _____ Hand me the mop.
   C. _____ Will you hand me the mop?

ANALOGIES:
Circle the correct answer:

5. disease : nausea :: earthquake : _____
   (a) time   (b) stabilizing   (c) movement   (d) California

SENTENCE COMBINING:

6. The moon is the only natural satellite of the Earth.
   The moon takes 27.3 days to rotate around the Earth.

   _____

   _____

CAPITALIZATION:

1. were german submarines used during world war I?

PUNCTUATION:

2.

                                        Post Office Box 25022
                                        Madison WI 53701
                                        March 4 20--
        Dear Joy
                Matt Chrissy and I bought a new horse last night
                                        Your niece
                                        Lucy

PARTS OF SPEECH: PRONOUNS
  Circle the correct pronoun:

3.   During the debate, (we, us) students had to pay close attention to each speaker.

SENTENCE TYPES:
  Change this interrogative sentence to an exclamatory one:

    Will you stop that?

4.   _____

SPELLING:
Remember: Words ending in vowel + vowel + consonant (VVC) do not usually change
        when adding a suffix.   Example: greet + er = greeter
                Words ending in consonant + consonant + <u>e</u> (CCe) usually drop the <u>e</u>
        when adding a suffix beginning with a vowel.
                Example: huddle + ing = huddling
  Write the correct spelling of these words:

5.   A.   demand + ing - _____

     B.   coil + ing - _____

     C.   rust + ic - _____

SENTENCE COMBINING:

6.   The model has shiny white teeth.
     The model's smile dazzles everyone.

DAY 84

CAPITALIZATION:

1.　the british architect, sir joseph paxton, built london's famous crystal palace.

PUNCTUATION:

2.　Can koi a type of tropical fish live to be over two hundred years old

PARTS OF SPEECH:　VERBS
　　Circle the correct verb:

3.　A.　Mr. Brody has not (brung, brought) his camera.

　　B.　Someone may have (written, wrote) the secret code.

　　C.　That diver has (swum, swam) since she was three years old.

CLAUSES:
　　　　A clause contains a subject and a verb.
　　　　An independent clause expresses a complete thought.
　　　　　　Example:　He always gargles for thirty seconds.
　　　　A dependent clause does not express a complete thought.
　　　　　　Example:　Before the new hotel was built
　　　Write IC if the clause is independent; write DC if the clause is dependent:

4.　A.　_____　When the sun slid behind a cloud in the middle of the afternoon.

　　B.　_____　Their hands were chapped from the cold and wind.

SPELLING:
　　Write the correct spelling of these words:

5.　A.　flash + ing - _____

　　B.　paddle + ed - _____

　　C.　bubble + ing - _____

SENTENCE COMBINING:

6.　Alana is a photographer.
　　She specializes in children's portraits.

_____

_____

CAPITALIZATION:

1. during the revolutionary war, samuel adams led the boston tea party.

PUNCTUATION:

2. Havent you ever met these triplets Nick Nicole and Nina

PARTS OF SPEECH: NOUNS
   Write the possessive:

3. a quilt belonging to Grandmother: _____

PREFIXES/ROOTS/SUFFIXES:
   **A root is a base from which words are formed. Some roots can
   stand alone as a word; some form only a part of a word.**
   Equine **is from the Latin word** *equus* **meaning horse.**

4. If someone mentions that he will be spending the day with his equine friend, he

    would probably be spending it _____.

SPELLING:

   Write the correct spelling of these words:

5. A.   baby + ed - _____
    B.   baby + ing - _____
    C.   strap + ing - _____

SENTENCE COMBINING:

6. The rain ceased in the early morning.
    The sun shone for the rest of the day.

    _____

    _____

DAY 86

CAPITALIZATION:

1. the poet, henry wadsworth longfellow, was a professor at bowdoin college in maine.

PUNCTUATION:

2. Well these rocks of course arent valuable   said Cam mildly

DICTIONARY SKILLS: ALPHATBETIZING

Write these words in alphabetical order:

3. story   paste   stare   track   pasta   range

PARTS OF SPEECH: NOUNS

An indirect object is the receiver of *some* direct objects.   You can insert <u>to</u> or <u>for</u> mentally before an indirect object.

to   I.O.   D.O.

Example: Mario handed / the customer a sundae.

Underline the subject once and the verb or verb phrase twice.   Label the direct object - <u>D.O.</u> and the indirect object - <u>I.O.</u>:

4. The postal worker sold me a special stamp.

ANALOGIES:

Circle the correct answer:

5. bride : wife :: groom : _____
    (a) horse   (b) father   (c) usher   (d) husband

SENTENCE COMBINING:

6. Ellis Island is in the harbor of New York.
    It once was an examination center for immigrants to America.

    _____

    _____

CAPITALIZATION:

1. having developed pneumonia, she entered nordic medical center last february.

PUNCTUATION:

2. Ive mentioned that youre not pleased with their decision   said Mrs Korte

PARTS OF SPEECH: CONJUNCTIONS/INTERJECTIONS
   Box any interjections; circle any coordinating conjunctions:

3. Whew! That car slid on ice but it didn't hit the chunky post or the tree!

SENTENCES/FRAGMENTS/RUN-ONS:
   Write S if the words form a sentence; write F for fragment if the words do not form a sentence:

4. A. _____ Chessa and I rarely that.
   B. _____ Please don't mumble.

ANALOGIES:
   Circle the correct answer:

5. flashlight : illuminate :: disinfectant : _____
   (a) purify   (b) infect   (c) fester   (d) disperse

SENTENCE COMBINING:

6. Angling means fishing with a rod.
   Angling also means fishing with a reel.
   It also means fishing with a line.
   It also means fishing with a lure.

_____

_____

DAY 88

CAPITALIZATION:

1. on valentine's day, mom and aunt beth gave us misty* marshmallows.

*brand name

PUNCTUATION:

2. No I shouldnt be surprised that her name in the telephone book is listed as Po T K

PARTS OF SPEECH: ADVERBS
Circle the correct adverb:

3. Lynn spoke (more clearly, most clearly) during her second speech.

PREFIXES/ROOTS/SUFFIXES:
Prefixes help to understand word meanings:

pseudo - false (pseudopod)   **super - above, highest (super**man)
anti - against (antifreeze)   **multi, poly - many (multi**ply); (**poly**graph)

Write an appropriate prefix:

4. A. Their apartment _____intendent had their plumbing fixed.
   B. Another word for a fake name is _____nym.
   C. We like _____grain cereal.
   D. In geometry, the class studies many sided figures or _____gons.

ANALOGIES:
Circle the correct answer:

5. wrongly : incorrectly :: impulsively : _____
   (a) understanding   (b) forcefully   (c) reluctantly   (d) hastily

SENTENCE COMBINING:

6. A basket of dried flowers fell to the floor.
   The dried flowers crumbled.

_____

_____

DAY 89

CAPITALIZATION:

1. his dad cooked belgian waffles at a lion's club breakfast.

PUNCTUATION:

2. By the way the following streets are closed Ash Place Lazy Lane and Ruby Drive

PARTS OF SPEECH: ADVERBS
Circle any adverbs that tell *how* or *when*:

3. Ty and Chessa played soccer well today.

PARTS OF SPEECH: NOUNS
Nouns ending in *ay, uy, ey,* and *oy* usually add s to form the plural. Nouns ending in consonant + y, usually change the *y* to *i* and add es to form the plural.
Write the plural of each noun:

4. A. jay - _____   D. alloy - _____

    B. donkey - _____   E. guppy - _____

    C. history - _____   F. lullaby - _____

ANALOGIES:

Circle the correct answer:

5. shivering : shaking :: leaning : _____
    (a) skiing   (b) upright   (c) capsizing   (d) sailing

SENTENCE COMBINING:

6. Cuckoos are grayish-brown birds.
    They lay eggs in the nests of other birds.

    _____

    _____

DAY 90

CAPITALIZATION:

1. we drove on natchez trace parkway which originally was a native american trail.

PUNCTUATION:

2. If you agree   said Mrs Leon   please raise your hand

SUBJECT/VERB:

Underline the subject; circle the verb that agrees with the subject:

3. The handles of the chest (needs, need) to be replaced.

PREFIXES/ROOTS/SUFFIXES:

A root is a base from which words are formed. Some roots can stand alone as a word; some form only a part of a word.

Vigor is a Latin root that means make strong.

Write a sentence using the word, *vigorous:*

4. _____

ANALOGIES:

Circle the correct answer:

5. cut : scissors :: paint : _____
    (a) brush   (b) thinner   (c) picture   (d) wall

SENTENCE COMBINING:

6. We can go to the park.
    We must wait until our parents get home.

    _____

    _____

CAPITALIZATION:

1. i. vacation tours
   a. land
      1. bus
      2. train
   b. cruises

PUNCTUATION:

2. Toward the end of winter they visited their aunt in Washington D C

PARTS OF SPEECH: ADJECTIVES/ADVERBS
   Real **is usually an adjective meaning true, sincere, or genuine.**
   Really **is an adverb that tells** *to what extent.*

   Circle the correct word:

3. A. They are (real, really) excited about the game?
   B. Is this frame made of (real, really) teakwood?

FRIENDLY LETTERS/ENVELOPES:
   Write your return address on this envelope:

4. _____

   _____

   _____

   _____

   _____

ANALOGIES:
   Circle the correct answer:

5. jump : pounce :: cry : _____
   (a) sob   (b) tears   (c) laugh   (d) meow

SENTENCE COMBINING:

6. Monkey bread is the fruit of the African baobao tree.
   Monkey bread is eaten by monkeys.

_____

DAY 92

CAPITALIZATION:

Capitalize these lines of poetry by C. Sandburg:

1. maybe he believes me, maybe not,
   maybe i can marry him, maybe not.

PUNCTUATION:

2. Miss R Poshski
   2396 S Chrysler Dr
   Auburn Hills MI   48326

PARTS OF SPEECH: NOUNS

Write **C** if the noun is concrete; write **A** if the noun is abstract:

3. A. _____ battery   B. _____ bravery   C. _____ sink

PARTS OF SPEECH: ADVERBS

Circle the correct word:

4. I like this pancake syrup, but Yancy never seems to want (none, any).

ANALOGIES:

Circle the correct answer:

5. plunge : dive :: push : _____
   (a) pose   (b) pull   (c) nudge   (d) protest

SENTENCE COMBINING:

6. A waitress served muffins.
   The waitress was from England.
   The waitress spoke with a British accent.

   _____

   _____

CAPITALIZATION:
   Capitalize these titles:

1. A. "brilliant britain"
     B. "suburb on the green"
     C. <u>teachers are special</u>

PUNCTUATION:

2. By the end of the third quarter both teams coaches were shouting excitedly

DIRECT OBJECTS:
  Underline the subject once and the verb or verb phrase twice.
  Circle the direct object:
  Remember: Deleting prepositional phrases will simplify the sentence.

3. I must have left my package in the car.

PARTS OF SPEECH: VERBS
  Place a √ if the verb is regular:

4. A. ____ to find   C. ____ to buy   E. ____ to hide
     B. ____ to fine   D. ____ to cry   F. ____ to ride

ANALOGIES:
  Circle the correct answer:

5. cute : gorgeous :: scary : _____
    (a) fearful   (b) afraid   (c) story   (d) terrifying

SENTENCE COMBINING:

6. The child drew a picture.
    He drew a picture of a house.
    The house has two doors and no windows.

_____

_____

DAY 94

CAPITALIZATION:

1. "we played jump rope at penn's park," said molly.

PUNCTUATION:

2. Alli Id like to borrow your long silk scarf for a play

DICTIONARY SKILLS: GUIDE WORDS

Two guide words appear in boldfaced type at the top of each dictionary page. The first word listed is the first entry on that page. The second word is the last entry on that page.

Place a √ if the word will appear on a page with the guide words:
ace - artistic:

3. A. ___ acid   B. ___ artist   C. ___ academy   D. ___ arsenic

CLAUSES:

Write IC if the clause is independent; write DC if the clause is dependent:

4. A. _____ Whenever Briana recites a poem in front of her classmates.

    B. _____ Her cotton gloves were too thin to keep her hands very warm.

ANALOGIES:

Circle the correct answer:

5. mane : horse :: udder : _____
    (a) gland   (b) milk   (c) teat   (d) cow

SENTENCE COMBINING:

6. An ostrich is a swift-running bird.
    An ostrich is the largest bird.
    It is the most powerful bird.

    _____

    _____

CAPITALIZATION:

1.   yesterday, his mother helped to plant dutch tulips in hyde square near hume lane.

PUNCTUATION:

2.   The baker answered No this isnt a three layer cake

PARTS OF SPEECH: **NOUNS**
    Circle any nouns:

3.   On Monday, Kam hooked up his printer to his new computer.

PHRASES/CLAUSES:
    A phrase is a group of words.   Example: since Friday
    A clause contains a subject and a verb.
        Examples: <u>Is</u> this <u>pearl</u> real?

        <u>Alita</u> <u>loves</u> to surf.

    Write <u>P</u> if the words form a phrase; write <u>C</u> if the words form a clause:

4.   A. _____ From the very beginning
     B. _____ When Igor began to walk

ANALOGIES:
    Circle the correct answer:

5.   crop : wheat :: aircraft : _____
     (a) helicopter   (b) flying   (c) landing   (d) space

SENTENCE COMBINING:

6.   The patient waited in the doctor's office for an hour.
     The patient moaned softly.
     The patient was displeased.

     _____

     _____

DAY 96

CAPITALIZATION:

1. during the french and indian war, the iroquois indians helped the british troops.

PUNCTUATION:

2. Deans mother asked   Isnt your brother twenty nine

PARTS OF SPEECH: VERBS
   Circle the correct verb:

3. A. The sun has (risen, rose).
    B. Gusts of wind had (blew, blown) down the chimney.
    C. Have you ever (wore, worn) snowshoes?
    D. Those tomatoes were (grown, grew) in a greenhouse.
    E. Her spirits had (sank, sunk) when she heard the news.

PARTS OF SPEECH: PRONOUNS
   **Reflexive pronouns are *myself, himself, herself, yourself,
   ourselves, themselves,* and *itself*.**
   Theirselves and hisself are always incorrect.
   Write an appropriate pronoun:

4. She changed the tire _____.

ANALOGIES:
   Circle the correct answer:

5. heir : heiress :: hero : _____
    (a) knight   (b) heroess   (c) heroine   (d) lady

SENTENCE COMBINING:

6. Diana's doll has a porcelain head.
    Diana's doll is an antique.
    The porcelain head is cracked.

_____

_____

CAPITALIZATION:

1. is the english language spoken in the union of south africa?

PUNCTUATION:

2. Brandy youre first on my list   said Tate

PREFIXES/ROOTS/SUFFIXES:
    A suffix is an ending; it is added to a root.
    Ness* is a suffix that means *state of or condition of.

Using this information, explain the word, *happiness:*

3. _____

PARTS OF SPEECH: ADJECTIVES/ADVERBS
    Circle the correct word:

4. This red sweater will look (good, well) with black pants.

SIMPLE/COMPOUND/COMPLEX   SENTENCES:
    A compound sentence is made up of two (or more) complete thoughts.
    These thoughts could stand alone as separate sentences.
    The coordinating conjunctions, *and, but,* and *or* are usually used
    to join the parts of a compound sentence.
        Examples: This bucket is heavy, but I can carry it.
                    The answer is fifty, and Mira has that answer.

    Place a √ if the sentence is a compound sentence:

5. A. ____   Kurt closed his eyes, but he could not sleep.
    B. ____   Her grandmother grabbed her hand, squeezed it, and laughed.

SENTENCE   COMBINING:

6. A cucumber is a vine-growing fruit with a green rind.
    A cucumber tree is a North American magnolia tree.

    _____

    _____

DAY 98

CAPITALIZATION:

1. take interstate 10 and then go south on seventh street to reach bank one ballpark.

PUNCTUATION:

2. Alecs sister in law yelled clearly loudly and enthusiastically during the boat race

PARTS OF SPEECH: VERBS
   Write the contraction:

3. A.   she is - _____   D.   cannot - _____

    B.   I am - _____   E.   could not - _____

    C.   was not - _____   F.   you will - _____

PARTS OF SPEECH: ADJECTIVES/PRONOUNS
   Numbers may stand alone; they serve as pronouns.
        Example: **Five** were dressed in long gowns.
   Numbers may modify (go over to) a noun; then, they serve as
   adjectives.   Example: I saw **five** elk in the forest.   (five elk)

   Write P if the word serves as a pronoun; write A if the word serves as
   an adjective:

4. A.   _____   Devi asked me to wait **ten** minutes for her.

    B.   _____   There were **ten** in each box.

SPELLING:
   Write the correct spelling of these words:

5. A.   impure + ity - _____

    B.   nature + al - _____

    C.   spray + ing - _____

SENTENCE COMBINING:

6. Sandor was rummaging through his grandfather's old trunk.
    He was looking for antique clothes for a play.

    _____

    _____

CAPITALIZATION:

1. the dead sea in the middle east is one of the world's saltiest lakes.

PUNCTUATION:

2. A teachers conference   said Dr Oxnard is being organized by Mrs D Tang

PARTS OF SPEECH: NOUNS
> **Some nouns totally change when forming the plural.** child - children
> **Use a dictionary if you are uncertain.**

> **Write the plural:**

3. A. foot - _____   B. ox - _____   C. medium - _____

PARTS OF SPEECH: ADVERBS
> **Write the plural:**

4. I never seem to have (no, any) quarters for the vending machine.

SPELLING:
> **Remember: Words ending in vowel + vowel + consonant (VVC) do
> not usually change when adding a suffix.**
> > Example: reap + er = reaper

> **Words ending in consonant + consonant + e
> usually drop the e when adding a suffix beginning with
> a vowel.**   Example: saddle + ed = saddled

> **Write the correct spelling of these words:**

5. A. trouble + ing - _____
    B. lean + ed - _____
    C. riddle + ed - _____

SENTENCE COMBINING:

6. A male African elephant may grow up to thirteen feet tall.
    A male Asian elephant may grow up to eleven feet tall.

_____

_____

DAY 100

CAPITALIZATION:

1. pedro said, "look at my new german shepherd named boo."

PUNCTUATION:

2. Aren by the way saves one fifth of his salary

PARTS OF SPEECH: ADJECTIVES/ADVERBS
    Circle the correct answer:

3. That horse doesn't jump (good, well).

SYNONYMS/ANTONYMS/HOMONYMS:
    Homonyms are words that sound alike but are spelled differently.
    Synonyms are words that have similar meanings.
    Antonyms are words with opposite meanings.

4.   A.   A synonym for annoyed is _____.
     B.   A homonym for peddle is _____.
     C.   An antomym for prohibit is _____.

ANALOGIES:
    Circle the correct answer:

5. ointment : heal :: jack-in-the-box : _____
     (a) entertain   (b) clown   (c) toy   (d) child

SENTENCE COMBINING:

6. These tires are worn.
    These tires are dangerous.
    These tires are almost new.

    _____

    _____

CAPITALIZATION:

1. they ate chow mein, a chinese-american dish, at lotus restaurant.

PUNCTUATION:
> **If part of a sentence occurs after a city and country, place a comma also after the country.**
>> Example: Tim visited Oslo, Norway, during the summer.

2. Laylas grandparents traveled to Ensenada Mexico by bus

PARTS OF SPEECH: ADJECTIVES
> **A proper adjective is derived from a proper noun.**
>> Example: Proper Noun: **A**sia
>> Proper Adjective: **A**sian

> **Write the proper adjective:**

3. A. Canada - _____
    B. England - _____
    C. Mexico - _____

PARTS OF SPEECH: VERBS
> **Underline the subject once and the verb or verb phrase twice:**

4. Marta and her mother drive to town each Saturday and shop at a local market.

ANALOGIES:
> **Circle the correct answer:**

5. fragrant : unscented :: hostile : _____
    (a) friendly   (b) serving   (c) deserving   (d) unsociable

SENTENCE COMBINING:

6. A camel's hair brush is used by artists.
    It is made of hair from squirrels' tails.

    _____

    _____

DAY 102

CAPITALIZATION:

1. they visited hog island which is in northern virginia and on the atlantic ocean.

PUNCTUATION:

2. The mens swim team hasnt practiced at the Y M C A for several years

WORDS:
   Circle the correct word:

3. A. (Their, There, They're) reaction was surprising.
   B. The smaller puppy was barking, (to, too, two).
   C. (May, Can) I ask a question?

PARTS OF SPEECH: PRONOUNS
   Possessive pronouns show ownership.
   Possessive pronouns are: my, mine   our, ours   it, its
   his   their, theirs   whose
   her, hers   your, yours

   Write an appropriate possessive pronoun:
4. Marsh and Miki told _____ friend about the wrestling tournament.

ANALOGIES:
   Circle the correct answer:

5. cup : pint :: quart : _____
   (a) ounce   (b) liquid   (c) measurement   (d) gallon

SENTENCE COMBINING:

6. The baby is crying.
   The baby has a fever.
   The baby has an ear infection.

   _____

   _____

CAPITALIZATION:

1. "the populist party was formed to express american farmers' opinions,"   megan said.

PUNCTUATION:

Use underlining or quotation marks:

2. A. Amusement Park   (title of a poem)

   B. All Summer in a Day   (name of a short story)

   C. The Tigger Movie   (title of a movie)

SENTENCE TYPES:

Change this interrogative sentence to an imperative one:

   Will you hand me a wrench?

3. _____

PARTS OF SPEECH: VERBS

Write the contraction:

4. A. they are - _____   D. I will - _____

   B. will not - _____   E. cannot - _____

   C. he would - _____   F. here is - _____

ANALOGIES:

Circle the correct answer:

5. watt : brightness :: gram : _____
   (a) weight   (b) pound   (c) ounce   (d) measure

SENTENCE COMBINING:

6. This camping spot is quiet.
   It is secluded.
   Few people know about this camping spot.

_____

_____

DAY 104

CAPITALIZATION:

1. was jefferson davis elected the leader of the confederate states of america?

PUNCTUATION:

2.   7771 Neese Road
                                                       Woodstock GA 30188
                                                       April 12 20--

    Dear Andy
        Come join our fun filled day of balloon rides water
    games and a picnic We hope to see you soon
                                                       Your friend
                                                       Karen

SUBJECT/VERB:
Underline the subject once and the verb twice:

3. Lori tugged the bracelet's clasp and inserted the oval part.

PARTS OF SPEECH: NOUNS
**An indirect object is the receiver of *some* direct objects. You can
insert to or for mentally before an indirect object.**

                                    to   I.O.   D.O.
            Example: I gave / my father his gift.

**Underline the subject once and the verb or verb phrase twice.
Label the direct object - D.O. and the indirect object - I.O.:**

4. Jacy sent Amy a funny card.

ANALOGIES:
Circle the correct answer:

5. part : component :: choice : _____
    (a) division   (b) wisdom   (c) option   (d) complication

SENTENCE COMBINING:

6. Someone had forgotten to turn off the water.
    Our yard flooded.

    _____

    _____

CAPITALIZATION:

1. the organization of american states met friday in a latin american country.

PUNCTUATION:

2. Eduardo Chavez M D is all of the nurses favorite doctor

PARTS OF SPEECH: VERBS
   Write *present, past,* or *future:*

3. A. _____ Your aunt will arrive in ten minutes.
   B. _____ They grow radishes in their garden.
   C. _____ The teacher smiled at the children.

SENTENCES/FRAGMENTS/RUN-ONS:
   Write <u>S</u> if the words form a sentence; write <u>F</u> for fragment if the words do not form a sentence:

4. A. _____ Their dad cooks chili on cold evenings.
   B. _____ A rabid fox had been reported.

ANALOGIES:
   Circle the correct answer:

5. rope : tether :: tweezers : _____
   (a) tease   (b) pull   (c) cut   (d) splinter

SENTENCE COMBINING:

6. Two brothers ate lunch at a pizzeria.
   Before that, they did chores.
   They ate lunch with their cousin.

   _____

   _____

DAY 106

CAPITALIZATION:

1.
                                        9555 madison avenue
                                        new york, ny 10016   **(A)**
                                        july 13, 20--

    my dear cousin,   **(B)**

        did you know that the milky way galaxy is shaped

    like a spiral? we are studying it in science class.   **(C)**

                                        your friend,   **(D)**
                                        kino   **(E)**

PUNCTUATION:

2.   Are carp trout and salmon considered bony fish   asked Mano

FRIENDLY LETTERS:
    Label the friendly letter parts in number 1:

3.   A. _____   D. _____

     B. _____   E. _____

     C. _____

PARTS OF SPEECH: INTERJECTIONS
    Write a sentence; use an interjection:

4.   _____

SIMPLE/COMPOUND/COMPLEX SENTENCES:
    A compound sentence is made up of two or more independent
    clauses; these could stand alone as separate sentences.
        Example: You may go, but you must return by nine o'clock.

    Place a √ if the sentence is a compound sentence:

5.   A. ___   Lani closed the mystery book and laid it on the table by her bed.
     B. ___   The speaker lifted a bird, and the students watched intently.

SENTENCE COMBINING:

6.   A hammerhead can refer to a type of shark.
     A hammerhead is also an African bird.

     _____

     _____

CAPITALIZATION:

1.   on june 15, 1215, king john of england signed the magna carta.

PUNCTUATION:
   When two complete thoughts (independent clauses) are joined by a conjunction (*and, but, or*), they form a compound sentence.
   Place a comma before the conjunction.
       Example: Some people eat snails, <u>but</u> I don't like them.
              independent clause   independent clause

2.   You must eat your vegetables or you cant have pie or cake

SENTENCE TYPES:
   Write the sentence type:

3.   A.   _____   Do you like to paint?
     B.   _____   Please repeat after me.
     C.   _____   Their ceramic masks have been fired.

PARTS OF SPEECH: ADJECTIVES
   Circle the correct adjective:

4.   That is the (sillier, silliest) joke I've ever heard!

ANALOGIES:
   Circle the correct answer:

5.   food : famine :: rain : _____
     (a) flood   (b) hurricane   (c) drought   (d) whirlpool

SENTENCE COMBINING:

6.   A beagle is a small hound.
     It has a smooth coat.
     It is often used as a hunting dog.

     _____

     _____

DAY 108

CAPITALIZATION:

1. was okefenoke swamp in northern florida named by seminole indians?

PUNCTUATION:
Punctuate this outline:

2. I Wind storms
      A Hurricanes
      B Tornadoes
   II Snowstorms

PARTS OF SPEECH: CONJUNCTIONS
Circle any coordinating conjunctions:

3. After the theater performance, many stopped at a cafe and ate a late dinner.

PARTS OF SPEECH: NOUNS
Write C if the noun is common; write P if the noun is proper:

4. A. _____ HORSE   B. _____ PONY   C. _____ STALLION

ANALOGIES:
Circle the correct answer:

5. lawyer : attorney :: preacher : _____
    (a) sermon   (b) minister   (c) church   (d) altar

SENTENCE COMBINING:

6. Marco and Kammi attended an estate sale.
    They bought a screen.
    The screen is Oriental.

    _____

    _____

CAPITALIZATION:

1. go west on dreyer lane to rodrick stone company, grandma.

PUNCTUATION:

2. Ms Stella Holuba lives in a small rustic cottage near Frederick Maryland

PARTS OF SPEECH: NOUNS
   Place a √ if the noun forms the plural by adding s:

3. A. ___ collie   C. ___ gash   E. ___ glint
    B. ___ surrey   D. ___ doily   F. ___ trolley

PHRASES/CLAUSES:
   Write P if words form a phrase; write C if the words form a clause:

4. A. _____ From the very beginning
    B. _____ When Igor began to walk

SPELLING:
   A word ending in consonant + vowel + e usually drops the final e when adding a suffix beginning with a vowel. The e is usually not dropped if a suffix beginning with a consonant is added.
          Examples: rescue + ing = rescuing
                      toe + s = toes
   Write the correct spelling of these words:

5. A.   persue + ing - _____

    B.   tie + ed - _____

    C.   shoe + less - _____

SENTENCE COMBINING:

6.   This bracelet is silver.
     It has turquoise insets.
     It has scroll designs.

     _____

     _____

DAY 110

CAPITALIZATION:

1. in world religion class, janny learned that the christian faith is based on the teachings of jesus.

PUNCTUATION:

Write the abbreviation:

2. A. gallon - _____   B. foot - _____   C. boulevard - _____

PARTS OF SPEECH: ADVERBS

Circle any adverbs that tell *when* or *where*:

3. When it's cold, we often go somewhere for hot chocolate.

PARTS OF SPEECH: PRONOUNS

Circle the correct pronoun:

4. The clerk handed (we, us) shoppers coupons for toys.

ANALOGIES:

Circle the correct answer:

5. now : present :: ageless : _____
   (a) interrupted   (b) neutral   (c) ceasing   (d) eternal

SENTENCE COMBINING:

6. The toddlers played on the sandy beach.
   Their mother sat under an umbrella.
   Their mother read a magazine.

   _____

   _____

CAPITALIZATION:

1.   are morgan horses and chickens raised at willow mill farm?

PUNCTUATION:

2.   Youre without a doubt the teams best player exclaimed Ned

PARTS OF SPEECH: VERBS
   Circle the correct verb:

3.   A.   I may have (drove, driven) over a nail.
      B.   One thirsty guest had (drunk, drank) most of the lemonade.

PREFIXES/ROOTS/SUFFIXES:
   Prefixes help to understand word meanings.
   Some prefixes are used to express numbers.
      quad - 4 (quadruplets [four babies])
      quint, pent - 5 (quintuplets [five babies])
      hex - 6 (hexagon [six-sided figure])
      oct - 8 (octagon [eight-sided figure])
   Write an appropriate prefix:

4.   A.   Their grandfather had _____ruple bi-pass heart surgery.
      B.   An _____opus is a sea creature with eight tentacles.
      C.   The _____agon is a five-sided government building near Washington, D. C.

ANALOGIES:
   Circle the correct answer:

5.   dawn : sunrise :: dusk : _____
      (a) noon   (b) night   (c) daytime   (d) sunset

SENTENCE COMBINING:

6.   Trifle is an English dessert.
      Trifle has sponge cake in it.
      Trifle also contains fruit and whipped cream.

_____

_____

DAY 112

CAPITALIZATION:

1.   wave hill mansion overlooks the hudson river in new york's bronx*.
*name of a borough

PUNCTUATION:

2.   Arent we appealing the decision Mr Bodnar   asked his client

PARTS OF SPEECH: PRONOUNS
Reflexive pronouns are *myself, himself, herself, yourself, ourselves, themselves,* and *itself.*

<u>Theirselves</u> and <u>hisself</u> are always incorrect.

Write an appropriate pronoun:

3.   I want to create a special card _____.

PARTS OF SPEECH: NOUNS
An indirect object is the receiver of *some* direct objects. You can insert <u>to</u> or <u>for</u> mentally before an indirect object.

for   I.O.   D.O.
Example: Grandpa baked / our mom a cherry pie as a love gift.

Underline the subject once and the verb or verb phrase twice. Label the direct object - <u>D.O.</u> and the indirect object - <u>I.O.</u>:

4.   Their son bought them an oak bookcase.

ANALOGIES:
Circle the correct answer:

5.   beat : rhythm :: concept : _____
      (a) concern   (b) lunacy   (c) advertising   (d) idea

SENTENCE COMBINING:

6.   The coral snake is a small one.
      It is a poisonous one.
      It is related to the cobra.

_____

_____

CAPITALIZATION:

1. the lady bought a japanese rug at dazel company furniture with her eagle express credit card.

PUNCTUATION:

2. My mothers cousin came to visit from Dublin Ireland last fall

PARTS OF SPEECH: NOUNS
   Place a √ by the correct possessive form:

3. A. ___ Dans' mother-in-law   B. ___ Dan's mother-in-law

DIRECT OBJECTS:
   Underline the subject once and the verb or verb phrase twice. Label the direct object - D.O.

4. The company must have sent the wrong order to us.

SPELLING:
   You learned that a one syllable word ending with consonant + vowel + consonant (CVC) usually doubles the final consonant when adding a suffix beginning with a vowel. Example: sip + ing = sipping
   Words of two or more syllables ending in consonant + vowel + consona (CVC) usually do not double the final consonant when adding a suffix.
   Examples: button + s = buttons   partner + ing = partnering
   Write the correct spelling of these words:

5. A.   fret + ing - _____
    B.   holler + ed - _____
    C.   hammer + ing - _____

SENTENCE COMBINING:

6. Lida is quiet and shy.
    Her best friend is shy and quiet, also.
    Her best friend's name is Jemima.

_____

_____

DAY 114

CAPITALIZATION:

1. from 476-1450 a. d., a period of european history called the middle ages occurred.

PUNCTUATION:
Punctuate the parts of a friendly letter.

2.
                          13 Bond Street
                          London England
                          May 20 20--
   Dear Madison
        Im sending the book entitled Angel Unaware
                          Love
                          Pam

PARTS OF SPEECH: INTERJECTIONS

3. Write an example of an interjection: _____

PARTS OF SPEECH: VERBS
Unscramble the twenty-three helping verbs:

4. od - _____   yma - _____   slahl - _____   aws - _____
    sode - _____   gmhit - _____   lwil - _____   ewre - _____
    ddi - _____   stum - _____   nca - _____   eb - _____
    sah - _____   slohud - _____   si - _____   gineb - _____
    veah - _____   ldouc - _____   ma - _____   nebe - _____
    adh - _____   doluw - _____   rea - _____

SPELLING:
Write the correct spelling of these words:

5. A. cantor + ing - _____
    B. scrub + ed - _____
    C. rapid + ly - _____

SENTENCE COMBINING:

6. A peanut is a legume.
   The peanut pod grows underground.

   _____

   _____

CAPITALIZATION:

Capitalize this friendly letter:

1.
                                73354 harrison street
                                topeka, ks 66603   **(A)**
                                november 2, 20--

dear trevor,   **(B)**
     would you like to go to the pacific northwest with us?   **(C)**
                             my regards,   **(D)**
                             josh   **(E)**

PUNCTUATION:

2.   I believe said Ramon that youre leaving at 3 15

FRIENDLY LETTER:

Label the parts of the friendly letter in #1:

3. A. _____   D. _____
      B. _____   E. _____
      C. _____

PARTS OF SPEECH: **NOUNS**

4.   Nouns ending with ____, ____, ____, ____, and ____ add <u>es</u> to form the plural.

ANALOGIES:

Circle the correct answer:

5.   impractical : realistic :: pleasant : _____
     (a) offensive   (b) foremost   (c) polite   (d) foreign

SENTENCE COMBINING:

6.   Aleta's first reaction was panic.
     Aleta sat down and closed her eyes.

_____

_____

DAY 116

CAPITALIZATION:

1. i. books
    a. mysteries
        1. fiction
        2. nonfiction
    b. historical romances
   ii. magazines

PUNCTUATION:

2. The M C Kraft Co has moved to 33 Trellis Dr St Louis Missouri

PARTS OF SPEECH: PRONOUNS
   Circle the correct pronoun:

3. The postcard from Chiko and (I, me) should have arrived last week.

PARTS OF SPEECH: NOUNS
   Circle any nouns:

4. In March, Tessa and she are traveling to Boston by train.

ANALOGIES:
   Circle the correct answer:

5. mollusk : clam :: reptile : _____
   (a) invertebrate   (b) spine   (c) alligator   (d) snail

SENTENCE COMBINING:

6. Sir Arthur Conan Doyle was an English physician and novelist.
   He wrote Sherlock Holmes stories.

   _____

   _____

CAPITALIZATION:

1. the jackson historical society held a sunday afternoon picnic at caledonia state park last may.

PUNCTUATION:

2. During John F Kennedys presidency many Americans joined the Peace Corp

PARTS OF SPEECH: ADVERBS
   Circle the correct adverb:

3. The beagle chewed the third bone (more noisily, most noisily).

WORDS:
   Circle the correct word:

4. A.   She (don't, doesn't) need any help.
   B.   Let me know when (your, you're) ready.

ANALOGIES:
   Circle the correct answer:

5. yard : distance :: degree : _____
   (a) temperature   (b) hot   (c) thermometer   (d) temperate

SENTENCE COMBINING:

6. Our picnic has been canceled.
   It has been canceled due to rain.
   It has been scheduled for next week.

   _____

   _____

DAY 118

CAPITALIZATION:

1. the phoenix suns* played at memorial coliseum for many years.
*name of a basketball team

PUNCTUATION:

2. Elizabeth asked Havent you been to Madrid Spain in the summer

PARTS OF SPEECH: NOUNS
Write C if the noun is concrete; write A if the noun is abstract:

3. A. _____ sword   B. _____ sorrow   C. _____ feeling

FRIENDLY LETTER ENVELOPES:
Write your return address:

4. _____

    _____
    _____
    _____

                            D. J. Lewis
                            12 Kauai Beach Drive
                            Lihue, HI   96766

_____

ANALOGIES:
Circle the correct answer:

5. quadrilateral : rectangle :: rock : _____
    (a) machete   (b) granite   (c) field   (d) balsa

SENTENCE COMBINING:

6. Abbie had her picture taken at a pillory.
    The pillory is located in historic Williamsburg, Virginia.

_____

_____

CAPITALIZATION:

1. last fall, judge wing visited lightner museum and a spanish fort in st. augustine.

PUNCTUATION:

2. Chessa and Don lived in Lake Tahoe Nevada for twenty one years

PREFIXES/ROOTS/SUFFIXES:

    Sculpt is from the Latin root, scupere, meaning to carve.
Using this information, explain the word, *sculpture:*

3. _____

SENTENCE TYPES:

Write an interrogative sentence:

4. _____

ANALOGIES:

Circle the correct answer:

5. chilly : icy :: hungry : _____
    (a) food   (b) hunger   (c) starving   (d) refueling

SENTENCE COMBINING:

6. An oval ball is used in Rugby football.
    The ball may be passed or carried.
    It may also be dribbled with the feet.

    _____

    _____

DAY 120

CAPITALIZATION:

1. in biology class at a local high school, students learned about mendel's study.

PUNCTUATION:

2. Mr Cord her kindergarten teacher spoke at a volunteers luncheon

WORDS:
   Circle the correct word:

3. A. Someone gave (their, there, they're) mother some oranges.
    B. I have a (real, really) bad headache.
    C. (To, Too, Two) much sugar isn't healthy.
    D. We know that (their, there, they're) coming to the brunch.

PARTS OF SPEECH: VERBS
   Place a √ if the verb is regular:

4. A. _____ to loop   C. _____ to teach   E. _____ to send
    B. _____ to lose   D. _____ to preach   F. _____ to mend

ANALOGIES:
   Circle the correct answer:

5. quilt : warmth :: shield : _____
    (a) strike   (b) battle   (c) metal   (d) protection

SENTENCE COMBINING:

6. Mrs. Hanson inherited a car.
    It is a 1935 car.
    The car won't start.

    _____

    _____

CAPITALIZATION:

1.   the federalist party was started by alexander hamilton in washington, d. c.

PUNCTUATION:

2.   1 S Stratton Street
                                             Gettysburg PA 17325
                                             May 20 20--
        Dear Gregg
             The boys wrestling team from our high school will
        compete next week in Durango Colorado
                                             Your friend
                                             Paco

PARTS OF SPEECH: ADJECTIVES/ADVERBS
     Circle the correct word:

3.   A.   This math problem is (real, really) hard.
     B.   Allison plays golf (well, good) for a beginner.

PARTS OF SPEECH: NOUNS
     Circle any nouns:

4.   The woman greeted us at the castle and gave a tour of its moat, dungeon, and tower.

ANALOGIES:
     **Analogies may express place relationships. Determine how the first
     two words are related. Then, find the answer that relates in the same
     way to the third word.**
                    Never : forever :: past : _____
                    (a) future   (b) yesterday   (c) weekly   (d) decidedly
        Never is the opposite of *forever*. The *past* is opposite of the *future*.

     Circle the correct answer:

5.   dawn : sunrise :: dusk : _____
     (a) noon   (b) night   (c) daytime   (d) sunset

SENTENCE COMBINING:

6.   Elba is a small Italian island in the Tyrrhenian Sea.
     It was the site of Napoleon's exile.

_____

_____

DAY 122

CAPITALIZATION:

1. has aunt nicole bought princess ice cream or <u>birds and bears</u>* at miracle market on tenth street?

*name of a magazine

PUNCTUATION:

2. Mr Gores silk flowered tie with tropical birds looked great with his three piece suit

SUBJECT/VERB:

With either/or and neither/nor, make the verb agree with the subject a𝖿𝗍𝖾𝗋 <u>or</u> or <u>nor</u>.

Example: Neither <u>Micah</u> *nor* his <u>sisters</u> (<u>eat</u>, eats) spinach.

Underline the subject once; underline the verb twice:

3. Neither her dog nor her cats (like, likes) to travel in a car.

PARTS OF SPEECH: ADJECTIVES
Circle any descriptive adjectives:

4. We made enormous chocolate milkshakes and chicken sandwiches for lunch.

SIMPLE/COMPOUND/COMPLEX   SENTENCES:
Place a √ if the sentence is a compound sentence:

5. A. ____   On Saturdays, Seth usually hikes and explores for an hour.
    B. ____   Dakota motioned to the travelers, but they didn't respond.

SENTENCE   COMBINING:

6. His grandfather was a soldier in World War II.
    His grandfather was part of the famous Normandy Invasion.

_____

_____

CAPITALIZATION:

Capitalize these titles:

1. A.   "teen angel"

    B.   "out of the wilderness"

    C.   "the back page"

PUNCTUATION:

2.   The book entitled Two Pennies for Parker was a short funny novel

PARTS OF SPEECH: VERBS

Write _present, past,_ or _future_:

3. A.   _____   Carlotta asks so many questions.

    B.   _____   The gold ore sparkled in the sun.

    C.   _____   Will you buy a microscope with your money?

DICTIONARY SKILLS: GUIDE WORDS

Place a √ if the word will appear on a page with the guide words:
party - praise:

4. A. ___ panic   B. ___ porous   C. ___ pram   D. ___ pastel

ANALOGIES:

Circle the correct answer:

5.   haiku : poetry :: bonsai : _____
     (a) plant   (b) wrestling   (c) Japan   (d) story

SENTENCE COMBINING:

6.   Sarah is a journalist.
     She wrote an article about saving whales.
     The article won an award.

     _____

     _____

DAY 124

CAPITALIZATION:

1. a vicksburg parade honored those whose ancestors fought in the civil war.

PUNCTUATION:

2. The producer the director and the script writer discussed the movies length

PARTS OF SPEECH: ADJECTIVES/PRONOUNS
Indefinites such as *some, few, many,* **and** *any* **may stand alone; they serve as pronouns.**
          Example: **Some** were dressed in long gowns.
Indefinites such as *some, few, many,* **and** *any* **may modify (go over to) a noun; then, they serve as adjectives.**
          Example: **Some** ducklings swam on the lake.   (Some ducklings)

Write P if the word serves as a pronoun; write A if the word serves as an adjective:

3. A. _____ Do you want **some**?   B. _____   I would like **some** mashed potatoes.

DICTIONARY: ALPHABETIZING
Place these word in alphabetical order:

4. mercy   prance   noisy   nosy   notary   practice   merchant

SPELLING:
Write the correct spelling of these words:

5. A.   can + ing - _____
    B.   cane + ing - _____
    C.   hibernate + ion - _____

SENTENCE COMBINING:

6. Pago Pago is a seaport.
    It is located on Tutuila Island.
    Tutuila Island is part of American Samoa.

   _____

   _____

CAPITALIZATION:

1. at alpine german restaurant, sauerbraten and austrian potato salad are served.

PUNCTUATION:
>   **When two or more complete thoughts (independent clauses) are joined by a conjunction such as *and, but,* or *or*, they form a compound sentence. Place a comma before the conjunction.**
>>   Examples: They may drive very late, **or** they may get a motel room at dusk.
>>   Rica sang, Marla played the guitair, **and** Pia whistled.

2. Her foot was badly sprained and she was taken to her doctors office

PARTS OF SPEECH: VERBS
   Write the contraction:

3. A.   are not - _____   D.   where is - _____

   B.   I will - _____   E.   will not - _____

   C.   would not - _____   F.   we are - _____

PARTS OF SPEECH: ADJECTIVES/ADVERBS
   Circle the correct word:

4. That candle smells (good, well).

SIMPLE/COMPOUND/COMPLEX   SENTENCES:
   Place a √ if the sentence is compound:

5. A.   _____   Devi could't find canned frosting, but she made her own.

   B.   _____   Aren listened carefully and wrote his name at the top of the paper.

SENTENCE   COMBINING:

6. Ben Franklin was the peacemaker at the Constitutional Convention.
   Ben Franklin later became the first Postmaster General of the United States.

   _____

   _____

DAY 126

CAPITALIZATION:

1. the corporate lawyer visited the southern part of alabama and stayed in a hotel on the gulf of mexico.

PUNCTUATION:

2. Yes Dan they live at the base of those high snow covered peaks

PARTS OF SPEECH: PRONOUNS
  Circle the correct word:

3. Tom finished the house painting (himself, hisself).

PREFIXES/ROOTS/SUFFIXES:
  Ous is a suffix that means possessing, full of, or characterized by.
  Using this information, explain the word, glamorous:

4. _____

SIMPLE/COMPOUND/COMPLEX   SENTENCES:
  Place a √ if the sentence is a simple sentence:

5. A. ____ The seasick man grasped the railing and nearly collapsed.
    B. ____ His hair was freshly washed, and he rubbed it with a towel.

SENTENCE COMBINING:

6. Some children are sledding.
    Some children are building a snowman.

    _____

    _____

CAPITALIZATION:

1. "have you," asked lars, "been to waterpocket canyon in utah?

PUNCTUATION:
Punctuate the following:

2. A. Visions in Charcoal (a magazine article)
   B. A Butterfly for Parkie (a story)
   C. Air Force 1 (an airplane)

SUBJECT/VERB:
Underline the subject; circle the verb that agrees with the subject:

3. One of my friends (is, are) very funny.

PARTS OF SPEECH: NOUNS
Write the possessive:

4. an office shared by two ministers: _____

ANALOGIES:
Circle the correct answer:

5. appetizing : tempting :: arid : _____
   (a) deodorize (b) dry (c) inviting (d) sharp

SENTENCE COMBINING:

6. Alicia's brother and sister ate all of the cookies.
   The cookies were chocolate chip.
   Alicia had just baked the cookies.

   _____

   _____

DAY 128

CAPITALIZATION:

1. is castle chillon on lake leman at the base of the swiss alps in europe?

PUNCTUATION:

2. Pippas name if Im correct was listed alphabetically as Swesey Pippa

SENTENCES/FRAGMENTS/RUN-ONS:
 Write <u>S</u> if the words form a sentence; write <u>F</u> for fragment if the words do not form a sentence:

3. A. _____ Although the fire went out.
    B. _____ Those boat shoes should prevent slipping.

PARTS OF SPEECH: NOUNS
 Nouns ending in <u>o</u> add s or es to form the plural. If you are not sure, use a dictionary. If the word should add *es*, the entry will list *pl. es.* Otherwise, add *s*.

 Write the plural:

4. A. moo - _____   B. tomato - _____   C. ego - _____

ANALOGIES:
 Circle the correct answer:

5. healthy : diseased :: trivial : _____
    (a) nervous   (b) forceful   (c) common   (d) crucial

SENTENCE COMBINING:

6. The house was designed by Ludwig Mies.
    It is located in Chicago.
    It is on steel piers.

    _____

    _____

CAPITALIZATION:

1. is mt. elbert the highest peak of colorado's sawatch mountains?

PUNCTUATION:
>   **If two describing adjectives joined by a conjunction *(and, but, or)* begin a sentence, place a comma after them and before the subject.**
>   Example: *Lost* and *hungry*, the <u>travelers</u> were happy to see a light.

2. Peppy and smiling several cheerleaders ran onto the stage

CLAUSES:
>   **Write <u>IC</u> if the clause is independent; write <u>DC</u> if the clause is dependent:**

3. A. _____ Kevin laughed.

    B. _____ If you need anything.

SYNONYMS/ANTONYMS/HOMONYMS:

4. A. A synonym for elastic is _____.

    B. An antonym for elastic is _____.

ANALOGIES:
>   **Circle the correct answer:**

5. inch : foot :: ounce : _____
    (a) centimeter   (b) pound   (c) ton   (d) kilogram

SENTENCE COMBINING:

6. The flying fox is a type of bat.
    It eats fruit.
    It lives in Africa.
    It also lives in Asia.
    It also lives in Australia.

    _____

    _____

DAY 130

CAPITALIZATION:

1. in science class, i learned that the okapi is an african animal similar to a giraffe.

PUNCTUATION:
Use underlining or quotation marks:

2. A. Back from Mars (title of a poem)
   B. Camping Life (title of a magazine)
   C. Vertebrates (title of a chapter)

PARTS OF SPEECH: ADJECTIVES/ADVERBS
Circle the correct word:

3. This baked apple smells (good, well).

PARTS OF SPEECH: NOUNS
Write the possessive:

4. an inn owned by two brothers: _____

ANALOGIES:
The second word of an analogy may describe the first or show a characteristic or feature of the first.
Example: sandpaper : rough :: satin : _____
(a) fabric   **(b) soft**   (c) gown   (d) blue

Circle the correct answer:

5. elephant : immense :: chihuahua : _____
   (a) dog   (b) Mexico   (c) unusual   (d) diminutive

SENTENCE COMBINING:

6. William Henry Harrison was the ninth President of the United States.
   He was called Tippecanoe.

   _____

   _____

CAPITALIZATION:

1. "my aunt," said jo, "visited chester county and brandywine valley last spring."

PUNCTUATION:
   Two complete thoughts that are about the same topic can be joined with a semicolon (;).
   Example: Matt went to a movie; his sister went to a hockey game.

2. Mrs Uman makes baskets youll find them at craft shows at the M T A* building

*abbreviation for Medical Transportation Association

PARTS OF SPEECH: ADVERBS
   Circle any adverbs that tell *where* or *how:*

3. The chef carefully cut wedges into the tomato and placed tuna within.

PREFIXES/ROOTS/SUFFIXES:
   Prefixes: **trans - across (trans**atlantic)   **micro - small (micro**scope)
                   semi - half (semipermanent)   **post - after, behind (post**nasal)
   Write an appropriate prefix:

4. A. Bacteria are _____organisms.
    B. The child drew a _____circle in the sand.
    C. Jana signed her name to the letter and added P.S. for _____script.
    D. That company _____ports furniture.

SPELLING:

   Write the correct spelling of these words:

5. A. casual + ty - _____   C. care + ful - _____
    B. care + ing - _____   D. rare + ity - _____

SENTENCE COMBINING:

6. The boy tripped over a garden hose.
    The boy fell on a wooden walkway.
    The boy broke his arm.

_____

_____

DAY 132

CAPITALIZATION:

1. my father and i like the negro spiritual entitled "swing low, sweet chariot."

PUNCTUATION:

2. Dad needs the following flour one third cup of sugar and apples

PHRASES/CLAUSES:
   Write **P** if words form a phrase; write **C** if the words form a clause:
   Remember: A clause contains a subject and a verb.

3. A. _____   Because we are making pancakes
    B. _____   Before the early morning traffic report

PARTS OF SPEECH: ADJECTIVES
   Write the proper adjective:

4. A. Alaska - _____
    B. Spain - _____
    C. Greece - _____

ANALOGIES:
   Circle the correct answer:

5. landform : peninsula :: vehicle : _____
    (a) car   (b) speed   (c) brake   (d) dealer

SENTENCE COMBINING:

6. The children are laughing.
    They are watching a show.
    The show is a puppet one.

    _____

    _____

CAPITALIZATION:
    Capitalize this friendly letter:

1.   12 north 56th street

                                             orange park, fl   32073

                                             june 2, 20--

    dear mrs. luna,

            my mother received the lifetime achievement award from a ser-
    vice club in raleigh, north carolina.

                                             sincerely,

                                             jolene

PUNCTUATION:
    Place a comma after an introductory participial phrase.
        Example: *Standing in line,* the child became restless.
                   Prompted by his mother, the child shook hands with me.

2.   Stuck in traffic the taxi driver looked for a faster quicker route

SUBJECT/VERB:
    Underline the subject once and the verb or verb phrase twice:

3.   On Saturday morning, Frank, John, and I are going to the skating rink.

PARTS OF SPEECH: PREPOSITIONS
    Box any object of the preposition:

4.   A shrill whistle sounded from a nearby building.

ANALOGIES:
    Circle the correct answer:

5.   penny : dollar :: year : _____
     (a) dime   (b) month   (c) decade   (d) century

SENTENCE COMBINING:

6.   A seahorse is a semitropical fish.
     It normally swims in an upright position.

_____

_____

DAY 134

CAPITALIZATION:

   Capitalize this outline:

1. i. american life
        a. colonial times
        b. modern times
    ii. british life

PUNCTUATION:

2.   No their grandparents twenty fifth anniversary wasnt celebrated on Dec 16 2000

DICTIONARY SKILLS: **ALPHATBETIZING**

   Place these words in alphabetical order:

3. attic   deal   antic   cattle   deem   antler

PARTS OF SPEECH: **VERBS**

   Circle the correct verb:

4. A. The runner has (stole, stolen) third base.
    B. Ice cubes had been (froze, frozen) in odd shapes.
    C. Have you ever (took, taken) a trip to Minnesota?
    D. He (seen, saw) a mouse run across the floor.
    E. Have you (ate, eaten) breakfast?

SPELLING:

   Write the correct spelling of the word:

5. A. stir + ed - _____   C. sweet + ly - _____
    B. freeze + ing - _____   D. annoy + ed - _____

SENTENCE COMBINING:

6. The couple visited Oatlands Plantation.
    Oatlands Plantation is an 1803 mansion in the South.

_____

_____

CAPITALIZATION:

1. the artist, william chase, helped to found the society of painters in pastel.

PUNCTUATION:
If two describing adjectives joined by a conjunction *(and, but, or)* begin a sentence, place a comma after them and before the subject.

Example: *Weary* and *tired*, the <u>woman</u> closed her eyes.

2. Happy and excited the children loaded the bus

PARTS OF SPEECH: VERBS
Underline the subject once and the verb or verb phrase twice:

3. Put your clothes into the washing machine.

SENTENCE TYPES:
Write a declarative sentence:

4. _____

ANALOGIES:
Circle the correct answer:

5. kangaroo : Australia :: penquin : _____
   (a) Arctic   (b) Antarctica   (c) Iceland   (d) Vinland

SENTENCE COMBINING:

6. The woman was upset.
   Her poodle was lost.
   She was searching the neighborhood for him.

_____

_____

DAY 136

CAPITALIZATION:

1. in june, the democratic party held a convention in new york city.

PUNCTUATION:

2. Our principal Tom Nast makes short snappy speeches

PARTS OF SPEECH: CONJUNCTIONS/INTERJECTIONS
      Circle any conjunctions;   box any interjections:

3.   Whoa! Slow down and tell me exactly what happened!

PARTS OF SPEECH: ADJECTIVES
      Circle the correct adjective:

4.   That dome is the (more unusual, most unusual) home in our neighborhood.

ANALOGIES:
      Circle the correct answer:

5.   dance : waltz :: tea : _____
      (a) coffee   (b) caffeine   (c) tannin   (d) herbal

SENTENCE COMBINING:

6.   The kitchen floor needs to be washed.
      The kitchen floor is caked with mud.

      _____

      _____

CAPITALIZATION:

1. samuel chase was an american revolutionary leader who later served on the u. s. supreme court.

PUNCTUATION:

2. Mr Greene said Fifty five people attended our horse lovers picnic

PARTS OF SPEECH: NOUNS
Write an example of a proper noun:

3. _____

PREFIXES/ROOTS/SUFFIXES:
Toxicum **is a Latin root that relates to poison.**
Using this information, explain the word, *nontoxic:*

4. _____

SPELLING:
Write the correct spelling of these words:

5.   A.   erode + ing - _____
    B.   flap + ed - _____
    C.   discreet + ly - _____
    D.   supply + ed - _____

SENTENCE COMBINING:

6.   The Gulf Stream is a warm ocean current.
    It flows from the Gulf of Mexico.

_____

_____

DAY 138

CAPITALIZATION:

1. the french explorer la salle claimed the mississippi valley and named it louisiana after king louis XIV.

PUNCTUATION:

2. Juanitas sister visited her mother in law in Lisbon Portugal last spring

PARTS OF SPEECH: PRONOUNS
   ### Circle the correct pronoun:

3. It was difficult for (we, us) participants to understand his oral directions.

SENTENCE TYPES:
   ### Change this declarative sentence to an interrogative one:
   Their mother let them go sledding in the afternoon.

4. _____

ANALOGIES:
   ### Circle the correct answer:

5. pimple : pus :: volcano : _____
   (a) eruption   (b) island   (c) spew   (d) lava

SENTENCE COMBINING:

6. A ceramic cup is for sale.
   The cup is shaped like a rabbit.
   It is for sale in a Victorian shop.

   _____

   _____

CAPITALIZATION:

1.
                                           22 green lake road
                                           st. george, utah 84790   **(A)**
                                           august 23, 20--

   dear deka,   **(B)**

PUNCTUATION:

2.   Jason Dill our neighbor restores antique furniture

FRIENDLY LETTER:

   Write the parts to the friendly letter in #1:

3.   A. _____   B. _____

PARTS OF SPEECH: ADJECTIVES/PRONOUNS

   This, that, those, and these may stand alone; they serve as pronouns.
          Example: **This** is a very strange situation.

   This, that, those, and these may modify (go over to) a noun; then, they serve as adjectives.
          Example: **This** book is science fiction.   (This book)

   Write P if the word serves as a pronoun; write A if the word serves as an adjective:

4.   A. _____   **Those** are my favorites!
     B. _____   **Those** pigs make so much noise.

ANALOGIES:

   Circle the correct answer:

5.   mistake : error :: lesson : _____
     (a) decrease   (b) teacher   (c) school   (d) instruction

SENTENCE COMBINING:

6.   Paisley is a colorful cloth pattern.
     Paisley is also a city in Scotland.

_____

_____

DAY 140

CAPITALIZATION:

Capitalize these lines from a poem entitled "Habits of a Hippopotamus" by Arthur Guiterman:

1. the hippopotamus is strong
    and huge of head and broad of bustle;

PUNCTUATION:

Write the abbreviation:

2. A. centimeter - _____   B. cup - _____   C. president - _____

PHRASES/CLAUSES:

Write P if words form a phrase; write C if the words form a clause:

3. A. _____ Dipping cookies into chocolate milk.
    B. _____ The toddler helps to make beds.

PARTS OF SPEECH: NOUNS

Write the possessive:

4. Arabian horses owned by several ladies: _____

SPELLING:

Write the correct spelling of these words:

5. A. delay + ing - _____   C. star + ing - _____
    B. adore + able - _____   D. taste + less - _____

SENTENCE COMBINING:

6. Haleakala National Park is on Maui.
    Maui is an island of Hawaii.
    A dormant volcano is there.

    _____

    _____

CAPITALIZATION:

1.   when nick had chicken pox, his cousin and i sent him castaway's* cookies.

*brand name

PUNCTUATION:
   Two complete thoughts that are about the same topic can be joined with a semicolon (;).
      Example: Dinner is nearly ready; we need to set the table.

2.   The cabin in the pines is isolated well need to take supplies

SUBJECT/VERB:

   With either/or and neither/nor, make the verb agree with the subject after *or* or *nor*.

      Example: Either my <u>mother</u> *or* my <u>aunts</u> (is, <u>are</u>) making lunch.

   Underline the subject once; underline the verb twice:

3.   Neither the driver nor the passenger (was, were) hurt in the accident.

PARTS OF SPEECH: **ADVERBS**
   Circle any adverbs:

4.   She stepped aside, took my hand reluctantly, and suddenly fell down.

ANALOGIES:
   Circle the correct answer:

5.   forceps : grasp :: mallet : _____
      (a) pound   (b) pour   (c) trowel   (d) pallet

SENTENCE COMBINING:

6.   An echidna is a spine-covered mammal.
      It is toothless.
      It eats ants with its sticky tongue.

_____

_____

DAY 142

CAPITALIZATION:

1. the greek poet named homer is supposed to have written in 700 b. c.

PUNCTUATION:

2. Bought by a racer the car was low to the ground sleek and fast

DIRECT OBJECTS:
    **Underline the subject once and the verb or verb phrase twice. Label
    the direct object - D.O.:**

3. Have you seen my jacket anywhere?

PARTS OF SPEECH: NOUNS
    Write the possessive:

4. A. a dog belonging to one boy - _____
    B. a dog belonging to four boys - _____

SPELLING:
    **A word ending with a single consonant + e usually makes the vowel
    before the consonant say its own name. A word ending with consonant +
    e usually drops the final e when adding a suffix beginning with a vowel.**
        Example: debate + able = debatable

    **However, if c or g occurs before the final e, the e is usually not
    dropped when adding the suffix, able.**

        Example: replace + able = replaceable
    Write the correct spelling of these words:

5. A. consume + able - _____
    B. recharge + able - _____
    C. love + able - _____

SENTENCE COMBINING:

6. Haute couture is the designing of ladies' high fashion.
    Haute cuisine is the preparing of fine foods.

    _____

    _____

CAPITALIZATION:

1. is the canadian remembrance day in november similar to the american veteran's day?

PUNCTUATION:

2. Kala Jose and she participated in the last event a three legged race

PARTS OF SPEECH: ADVERBS
   Circle the correct word:

3. You never have time for (nobody, anybody).

FRIENDLY LETTER ENVELOPES:
   Write your return address. Address the envelope to Kim Tsosie who lives in Philadelphia, PA. The street adress is 11542 North Third Street. The zip code is 19106.

4. _____

   _____
   _____
   _____

                              _____
                              _____
                              _____

   _____

SPELLING:
   Write the correct spelling of these words:

5. A. relative + ly - _____
   B. negate + ive - _____
   C. place + ment - _____

SENTENCE COMBINING:

6. Joel receives an allowance.
   Joel earns extra money by mowing his neighbors' lawns.

   _____

   _____

DAY 144

CAPITALIZATION:

1.   jill and jacy's new address is 23 justine drive, colorado springs, colorado.

PUNCTUATION:

2.   After a very long introduction Carol Tang R N spoke at the nurses conference

PARTS OF SPEECH: VERBS
    Write the twenty-three helping verbs:

3.   d_____   m_____   s_____   w_____
      d_____   m_____   w_____   w_____
      d_____   m_____   c_____   b_____
      h_____   sh_____   i_____   b_____
      h_____   co_____   a_____   b_____
      h_____   wo_____   a_____

PARTS OF SPEECH: NOUNS
    Circle any nouns:

4.   The bravery of the young knight was noticed by the king of his country.

ANALOGIES:
    Circle the correct answer:

5.   generous : greedy :: humble : _____
      (a) poor   (b) proud   (c) humility   (d) regal

SENTENCE COMBINING:

6.   Their dog has a long, shaggy coat.
      Their dog has long ears.
      Their dog is a cocker spaniel.

      _____

      _____

CAPITALIZATION:

1.   we visited the thomas point lighthouse on the chesapeake bay near annapolis.

PUNCTUATION:

2.   3 E King St
                          (A)   Shippensburg PA   17257
                                       Oct 23 20--
   (B)   Dear Aren
   (C)   Ive bought a home in Brussels Belgium   Lets get
                together to talk about it
                          (D)   Friends forever
                          (E)   Mary Rose

FRIENDLY LETTER:
   Label the parts of the above friendly letter:

3.   A. _____   D. _____
     B. _____   E. _____
     C. _____

PARTS OF SPEECH: NOUNS

4.   An example of a concrete noun is _____.

ANALOGIES:
   Circle the correct answer:

5.   topic : subject :: height : _____
     (a) tall   (b) elevate   (c) altitude   (d) alleviate

SENTENCE COMBINING:

6.   His parents went on a vacation.
     They went to Maine.
     They visited St. John Valley.
     It has many potato farms.

_____

_____

DAY 146

CAPITALIZATION:

1. this spring, clayton school students will travel on arctic airlines.

PUNCTUATION:
  Place a comma after an introductory participial phrase.
  Example: *Hurrying out of the rain,* I accidentally bumped into someone.
  Listed below appraisal, the house sold immediately.

2. Waiting for a shuttle bus the travelers eagerly discussed the groups plan for cook
  ing out

SENTENCES/FRAGMENTS/RUN-ONS:

Write S for sentence, F for fragment, and R-O for run-on:

3. A. _____ Left by the side of the road.
  B. _____ Jana stirred the soup, added some salt, and then added more, but she
  didn't think that the soup was flavorful so she added even more salt.

PARTS OF SPEECH: ADVERBS
  Circle the correct adverb:

4. At the city-wide competition, Anita threw the ball (farther, farthest).

ANALOGIES:
  Circle the correct answer:

5. fish : halibut :: decoration : _____
  (a) guest   (b) party   (c) festivity   (d) garland

SENTENCE COMBINING:

6. A door slammed.
  His dog became frightened.
  His dog hid under the bed.

  _____

  _____

CAPITALIZATION:

1. at a rodeo celebration, a group called silver heels played a song entitled "my friend for life."

PUNCTUATION:

2. Standing in line the lady read a book called Herbal Cooking

PARTS OF SPEECH: PRONOUNS

3. The personal pronouns that can serve as the subject of a sentence are _____, _____, _____, _____, _____, _____, and _____.

PREFIXES/ROOTS/SUFFIXES:

   Like **is a suffix that means** *similar to.*

   Use *childlike* **in a sentence***:*

4. _____

ANALOGIES:

   Circle the correct answer:

5. dash : stampede :: ravine : _____
   (a) rain   (b) canyon   (c) desert   (d) butte

SENTENCE COMBINING:

6. The teenager opened the refrigerator.
   The teenager took out cold meat and mustard.
   The teenager also took out lettuce and tomatoes.

   _____

   _____

DAY 148

CAPITALIZATION:

1. last winter, the torres family went to an aspen ski lodge for thanksgiving.

PUNCTUATION:

2. The class of 99 held its reunion many couldnt attended

SYNONYMS/ANTONYMS/HOMONYMS:

3. A. A synonym for strategy is_____.
    B. An antonym for conceal is _____.

PARTS OF SPEECH: ADJECTIVES/ADVERBS:
Circle the correct answer:

4. A. His new contact lenses don't work very (well, good).
    B. Is this a (real, really) scary show?

ANALOGIES:
Circle the correct answer:

5. lawful : illegal :: humorous : _____
    (a) radical   (b) witty   (c) serious   (d) joke

SENTENCE COMBINING:

6. Lani made an ice cream float
    She poured root beer into a tall glass.
    She then added ice cream.
    It was vanilla ice cream.

    _____

    _____

CAPITALIZATION:
Capitalize these lines of poetry by Robert Frost:

1. whose woods these are i think i know,
    his house is in the village though,

PUNCTUATION:

2. Did you Carlo become seasick due to the swirling choppy sea

PARTS OF SPEECH: VERBS
Write the verb or verb phrase:

3. A. _____   A cougar (past of *to growl*).
    B. _____   The salesman (future of *to present*) an offer.
    C. _____   Mora (present of *to take*) her lunch to work.

PARTS OF SPEECH: ADJECTIVES
Circle the correct adjective:

4. Cody is the (friendlier, friendliest) member of his family.

SIMPLE/COMPOUND SENTENCES:
A compound sentence is composed of two or more independent clauses (complete thoughts).   Example: <u>I like to skate</u>, but <u>I fall often</u>.

Write <u>S</u> if the sentence is simple; write <u>C</u> if the sentence is compound:

5. A. _____   The porter smiled, but she didn't open the door for us.
    B. _____   After we took our dogs for a walk, we made popcorn.

SENTENCE COMBINING:

6. Tessa will sell tickets for the medieval fair.
    Tessa cannot attend the fair.

    _____

    _____

DAY 150

CAPITALIZATION:

1. in world history class, i learned that president john f. kennedy started the peace corps, and many americans went to other countries to help.

PUNCTUATION:
Punctuate the following titles:

2. A. Good Morning to You   (title of a song)
    B. Wallace and Ladmo   (title of a television show)
    C. The ABC's of Hawaii   (title of a book)

PARTS OF SPEECH: ADJECTIVES/ADVERBS
Write ADJ. if the boldfaced word serves as an adjective; write ADV. if the boldfaced word serves as an adverb:

3. A. _____ They stood **nearby** while the tow truck driver checked their car.
    B. _____ A traveler stopped at a **nearby** farm house to ask for directions.

DICTIONARY SKILLS: GUIDE WORDS
Place a √ if the word will appear on a page with the guide words:
chess - chime:

4. A. ___ cheese   B. ___ chirp   C. ___ chimney   D. ___ chill

ANALOGIES:
Circle the correct answer:

5. refuge : haven :: ally : _____
    (a) opponent   (b) friend   (c) attendant   (d) supervisor

SENTENCE COMBINING:

6. A starfish has five arms arranged like the points of a star.
    A starflower is a white or pink five-petaled, star-shaped flower.

_____

_____

CAPITALIZATION:

1. hanover methodist church welcomed reverend ron boyd with a sunday brunch.

PUNCTUATION:
Two independent clauses (complete thoughts) about the *same* subject can be joined by a semicolon (;):
Example: Pam changed hair stylists; she now goes to Cute Cuts Salon.

2. Pippi did well on her algebra test shes been asked to tutor other students

PARTS OF SPEECH: VERBS
Circle the correct verb:

3. A.   Deka might have (ran, run) in the last race.
    B.   His mother could have (teached, taught) him to drive.
    C.   These glasses must have (broke, broken) in shipment.
    D.   I have never (lain, laid) on a feather bed.
    E.   The trainer has (thrown, threw) a treat to the dog.

PARTS OF SPEECH: ADJECTIVES
Circle any descriptive adjectives:

4. A brass antique urn was sitting on a small, hand-carved, cherry table.

ANALOGIES:
Circle the correct answer:

5. drill : bore :: vise : _____
    (a) advice   (b) pretend   (c) clamp   (d) screw

SENTENCE COMBINING:

6. Cape Horn is located at the tip of South America.
    It is known for its strong currents.
    It is also known for its stormy weather.

_____

_____

DAY 152

CAPITALIZATION:

Capitalize the following titles:

1. A. "home on the range"
   B. "as time goes by"
   C. "more is less"

PUNCTUATION:

2. Her name was listed in the commencement program as Ramos Misty S

PARTS OF SPEECH: NOUNS

Place a √ if the noun adds s to form the plural:

3. A. ___ flea   C. ___ logo   E. ___ branch   G. ___ wallaby
   B. ___ elk   D. ___ metal   F. ___ potato   H. ___ roof

PARTS OF SPEECH: VERBS

Write the contraction:

4. A. it is - _____   D. I would - _____
   B. do not - _____   E. might not - _____
   C. you have - _____ F. you are - _____

ANALOGIES:

Circle the correct answer:

5. likely : probably :: forlornly : _____
   (a) sadly   (b) possibly   (c) luckily   (d) continuously

SENTENCE COMBINING:

6. Trichinosis is a disease.
   Someone can get it from eating improperly cooked pork.

_____

_____

CAPITALIZATION:

1. "what do you know about the frog legs festival held in florida?" asked ria.

PUNCTUATION:
Use underlining or quotation marks:

2. A. the ship, Kristina Regina
    B. a nursery rhyme, Hey Diddle Diddle
    C. a magazine article, Home Is Where the Art Is

PARTS OF SPEECH: NOUNS
Underline the subject once and the verb or verb phrase twice. Label the direct object - D.O. and the indirect object - I.O.:

3. I must have given my brother the wrong baseball card.

PARTS OF SPEECH: ADJECTIVES/PRONOUNS
Write P if the boldfaced word serves as a pronoun; write A if the boldfaced word serves as an adjective:

4. A. _____   **Several** heifers roamed the meadow.
    B. _____   The teacher received **several** boxes of chocolate.

SPELLING:
Write the correct spelling of these words:

5. A. adventure + ous - _____
    B. sole + ly - _____
    C. stun + ing - _____
    D. purify + ed - _____

SENTENCE COMBINING:

6. The whelk is a large marine snail.
    It feeds on crabs.
    It also feeds on lobsters.

    _____

    _____

DAY 154

CAPITALIZATION:

1. did you attend the harney country carnival sponsored by volunteer firemen?

PUNCTUATION:

2. A womens club meeting was held at 1201 E Clay Street Richmond Virginia

PARTS OF SPEECH: PRONOUNS
   Circle the correct word:

3. They chose to build the cabin (themselves, theirselves).

PARTS OF SPEECH: ADJECTIVES
   Circle any adjectives:

4. Two frisky puppies and a gray hound played in the muddy, tree-lined meadow.

SIMPLE/COMPOUND SENTENCES:

5. Explain why this sentence is not a compound sentence.
     While Mrs. Smalley ate breakfast, she watched the stock report.

     _____

     _____

SENTENCE COMBINING:

6. Mr. Davis is a businessman.
    Mr. Davis ordered a briefcase and business cards.
    Mr. Davis ordered an answering machine.

     _____

     _____

CAPITALIZATION:

1. the governor asked, "is miss jordan new to the department of energy?"

PUNCTUATION:
   Use underlining or quotation marks:

2. A. In the Stoneworks   (title of a book)
    B. Good Morning, World   (name of a television show)
    C. Aging Kitties   (title of a newspaper article)

PARTS OF SPEECH: NOUNS
   Write the possessive:

3. A. toys belonging to Russ - _____
    B. cupcakes made by several brothers - _____

PREFIXES/ROOTS/SUFFIXES:
   There are five prefixes that are commonly used to express *not*: un, il, in, non, and im.
   Using each of the prefixes listed, write an appropriate prefix:

4. A. _____related   C. _____literate   E. _____coherent
    B. _____penetrable   D. _____toxic

ANALOGIES:
   Circle the correct answer:

5. cutlery : knife :: crime : _____
    (a) jail   (b) theft   (c) sheriff   (d) law

SENTENCE COMBINING:

6. A family reunion was held.
    Marco's aunt and uncle from Iowa attended.
    The reunion was held at South Mountain Fairgrounds.

    _____

    _____

DAY 156

CAPITALIZATION:

1. lulu said, "my father lives in the pacific northwest* near seattle."

*name of a region

PUNCTUATION:

2. Loni his brothers girlfriend will be arriving at 4 00 P M

PREFIXES/ROOTS/SUFFIXES:

3. A. Would a subcontractor be the main person in charge? _____
    B. Premedicate means to take medicine _____ receiving treatment.
    C. A dog that is black, tan, and white can be called a _____color.

PARTS OF SPEECH: ADVERBS
    Circle the correct answer:

4. We edited our stories (more carefully, most carefully) the third time.

ANALOGIES:
    Circle the correct answer:

5. commercial : sell :: newscast : _____
    (a) buy   (b) inform   (c) persuade   (d) demand

SENTENCE COMBINING:

6. A dugong is a tropical mammal.
    It lives off the Indian Ocean.
    It feeds mostly on seaweed.

_____

_____

CAPITALIZATION:

1. in the united states congress, the house of representatives is based on population.

PUNCTUATION:

2. My first grandchild said Sen Smith proudly was born on Monday January 1 2001

PHRASES/CLAUSES:
Write P if the words form a phrase; write C if the words form a clause:

3. A. _____ Although Thong doesn't like oysters.
    B. _____ The dog helped the shepherd with the lambs.

FRIENDLY LETTERS/ENVELOPES:
Write your return address on this envelope:

4. _____

    _____

    _____

    _____

    _____

ANALOGIES:
Circle the correct answer:

5. dense : sparse :: friendly : _____
    (a) hostile   (b) respected   (c) talkative   (d) amicable

SENTENCE COMBINING:

6. Hail pelted our vehicle.
    The hail was the size of marbles.
    We pulled off the road.

    _____

    _____

DAY 158

CAPITALIZATION:

1. did abraham lincoln write the emancipation proclamation during a stay at a cottage called anderson house?

PUNCTUATION:

2. Yes our canoe trip is Friday we want you to come Cole

SUBJECT/VERB:
Underline the subject once and the verb twice:

3. One of the boys leaned forward and grabbed my arm.

PARTS OF SPEECH: NOUNS
Write the possessive:

4. A. a craft show sponsored by a church - _____
    B. a basketball team for men - _____
    C. pastries made by chefs - _____

SPELLING:
Write the correct spelling of these words:

5. A. stripe + ed - _____   C. rely + ing - _____
    B. strip + ed - _____   D. rely + able - _____

SENTENCE COMBINING:

6. The house has been restored.
    It had been built in 1956.
    It is a ranch-style house.

    _____

    _____

CAPITALIZATION:

1. grandpa ngi read the article, "traveling during the winter," in <u>traveler's digest</u> magazine.

PUNCTUATION:

2. Jennifer will you go with me to Cody Wyoming sometime   asked Polly

SENTENCE TYPES:
   Write an imperative sentence:

3. _____

CLAUSES:
   Write <u>IC</u> if the clause is independent; write <u>DC</u> if the clause is dependent:

4. A. _____ Unless the gate is open.
   B. _____ The car rental was very cheap.

ANALOGIES:
   Circle the correct answer:

5. teeth : gum :: aorta : _____
   (a) ear   (b) lungs   (c) atrium   (d) heart

SENTENCE COMBINING:

6. The class voted.
   The class decided to take an essay test.
   Some students were perturbed.

   _____

   _____

DAY 160

CAPITALIZATION:

1. is hoover dam located on the colorado river in southern nevada?

PUNCTUATION:

2. His reply without a doubt surprised Randy his dad and his mother

PARTS OF SPEECH: PRONOUNS
   Circle the correct pronoun:

3. During each summer, Ria and (him, he) go to Idaho for a month.

PARTS OF SPEECH: ADVERBS/ADJECTIVES
   Circle the correct word:

4. He moved his hand so (quick, quickly) that I couldn't see what was in it.

ANALOGIES:
   Circle the correct answer:

5. pride : lion :: gaggle : _____
    (a) goose   (b) rooster   (c) choker   (d) joke

SENTENCE COMBINING:

6. The gorilla is the largest and most powerful ape.
    It is native to African jungles.

    _____

    _____

CAPITALIZATION:

1. with jefferson's louisiana purchase, america expanded from the mississippi river to the rocky mountains.

PUNCTUATION:

2. After the Memorial Day parade were staying with you until 4 00 Trisha

PARTS OF SPEECH: ADVERBS
   Circle any adverbs:

3. Juan answered so softly that I could not hear him well.

SENTENCES/FRAGMENTS/RUN-ONS:
   Write <u>S</u> for sentence, <u>F</u> for fragment, and <u>R-O</u> for run-on:

4. A. _____ Because she had a cold for nearly three weeks.
   B. _____ Noah had hiked all day he was exhausted.
   C. _____ Jina stuck her tongue out and made a funny face at the camera.

ANALOGIES:
   Circle the correct answer:

5. particularly : especially :: alertly : _____
   (a) attentively   (b) instantly   (c) sneakily   (d) dimly

SENTENCE COMBINING:

6. A bug scurried across the floor.
   It was an enormous black bug.
   Everyone left the room.

   _____

   _____

DAY 162

CAPITALIZATION:

1. her grandmother, a member of hill country club, does not participate in any halloween activities.

PUNCTUATION:

Punctuate this outline:

2. I Patterns
    A Geometric
    B Spiral
    II Blueprints

PARTS OF SPEECH: ADJECTIVES

Write the proper adjective:

3. A. Germany - _____

    B. Ireland - _____

    C. Europe - _____

PARTS OF SPEECH: CONJUNCTIONS

Write a sentence containing two conjunctions; circle them:

4. _____

ANALOGIES:

Circle the correct answer:

5. morsel : food :: shard : _____
    (a) card   (b) casserole   (c) pottery   (d) piece

SENTENCE COMBINING:

6. Our plans are to visit an art museum.
    We may visit a science museum instead.
    We will do this next Friday.

_____

_____

CAPITALIZATION:

1.   2 n michigan ave
                           (A)   chicago il
                                          nov 29 20--
    (B)   dear wes
                         our family went to the museum of northern arizona
    (C)   last summer   we learned that early indians of arizona
                 had turkeys and dogs as domesticated animals
                                          (D)   your cousin
                                          (E)   rosa

PUNCTUATION:

2.   Punctuate the above letter.

FRIENDLY LETTER:

   Label the parts of the above friendly letter:

3.   A. _____   D. _____
      B. _____   E. _____
      C. _____

PARTS OF SPEECH: INTERJECTIONS

   Write a sentence containing an interjection:

4.   _____

SPELLING:

   Write the correct spelling of these words:

5.   A.   atrophy + ed - _____

      B.   discern + ing - _____

      C.   ease + ment - _____

SENTENCE COMBINING:

6.   A koala is an Australian animal.
      It dwells in trees.
      It feeds exclusively on eucalyptus leaves and buds.

   _____

   _____

DAY 164

CAPITALIZATION:

  Capitalize this outline:

1. i. plant cell

         a. nucleus

         b. chloroplasts

     ii. animal cell

PUNCTUATION:

2. Pat Mahlan master of ceremonies handed Nicole Yassi D A the award

PARTS OF SPEECH: VERBS

  Write the verb or verb phrase:

3. A. _____ Her reaction (past of *to surprise*) us.
    B. _____ Mike (present of *to live*) in a college apartment.
    C. _____ Their wedding (future of *to be*) tomorrow.

PREFIXES/ROOTS/SUFFIXES:

  Vid is a root that relates to sight.

  Write a word that uses *vid* as a base and explain it:

4. _____

ANALOGIES:

  Circle the correct answer:

5. Africa : continent :: Florida : _____
    (a) tropics   (b) cape   (c) peninsula   (d) swamp

SENTENCE COMBINING:

6. Dr. Jones examined the patient.
    Dr. Jones wrote a prescription.
    The patient was a poodle.

    _____

    _____

CAPITALIZATION:

1. last week, mayor troon played the clarinet in our town's st. patrick's day parade.

PUNCTUATION:

2.
                                                            12893 W Summit Hill Dr
                                                            Knoxville TN 37902
                                                            February 28 2001

   Dear Aleta
        Peter is now twenty five years old   Its hard to believe that
   my talkative energetic toddler grew up so quickly
                                                            Yours truly
                                                            Marcy

PARTS OF SPEECH: ADJECTIVES
   Circle the correct adjective:

3. Their friend seemed (more frightened, most frightened) of the group.

SYNONYMS/ANTONYMS/HOMONYMS:
   Circle any synonyms for *clever*:

4. clever: (a) obstinate   (b) senseless   (c) foolish   (d) shrewd

SPELLING:
   Write the correct spelling of these words:

5. A. love + ly - _____   C. omit + ing - _____
    B. succeed + ed - _____   D. refuse + al - _____

SENTENCE COMBINING:

6. The pin is sterling.
    She inherited it from her grandmother.
    It has many tiny pearls around the edge.

   _____

   _____

DAY 166

CAPITALIZATION:

1. in october, we saw a painting by john singer sargent in the chicago museum of art.

PUNCTUATION:

2. Wow Lu has moved to 1 Easy Street Carefree Arizona and she has seen a scorpion

PARTS OF SPEECH: NOUNS
Write an example for each type of noun:

3. A. Common: _____
    B. Proper: _____
    C. Concrete: _____
    D. Abstract: _____

PARTS OF SPEECH: ADJECTIVES
Circle any adjectives:

4. That new model home has tall French doors and a granite kitchen counter.

ANALOGIES:
Circle the correct answer:

5. suggest : advise :: change : _____
    (a) modify   (b) rectify   (c) meditate   (d) crucify

SENTENCE COMBINING:

6. A redingote is a long coat.
    It opens down the front.
    It is full-skirted.

    _____

    _____

CAPITALIZATION:

1. the kalish family visited the chihuahuan desert in southeastern arizona.

PUNCTUATION:

2. Yes well go to Montezumas Castle my friend

SENTENCE TYPES:
    Write an exclamatory sentence:

3. _____

DIRECT OBJECTS:
    **Underline the subject once and the verb or verb phrase twice. Label
    the direct object - D.O.:**

4. During the silver anniversary party, Mrs. Lu hugged Rebecca and me.

SPELLING:
    **You have learned that words of two or more syllables ending in
    consonant-vowel-consonant (CVC) usually do not double the final
    consonant when adding a suffix.** Example: banter + ed = bantered

   Exception: **A two-syllable word ending in consonant-vowel-
                    consonant (CVC) usually doubles the final
                    consonant when adding a suffix beginning with
                    a VOWEL *if* the second syllable is accented.**

                    Example: be gin´ + ing = beginning

    Write the correct spelling of these words:

5. A.   forget + ing - _____

    B.   begin + er - _____

    C.   forget + ful - _____

SENTENCE COMBINING:

6. After dinner, Molly always rinses the plates.
    Melissa and Scott put leftovers in the refrigerator.

    _____

    _____

DAY 168

CAPITALIZATION:

1. the communist party under vladimir lenin took control of russia in 1917.

PUNCTUATION:

2. Your souvenir the small wooden carving will be your mothers favorite gift

PARTS OF SPEECH: ADVERBS
   Place a √ if the sentence is correct:

3. A. ____   Ivan doesn't ever spend any time with us.
    B. ____   We scarcely have no time to play.

FRIENDLY LETTERS:
   Use your address to write the heading of a friendly letter:

4.   _____
                                         _____
                                         _____

    Dear Seth,

SPELLING:
   Write the correct spelling of these words:

5. A. excel + ent - _____
    B. saucy + ness - _____
    C. pity + ing - _____

SENTENCE COMBINING:

6. The hostess welcomed the guest.
    The hostess introduced the guest to others at the gathering.

    _____

    _____

CAPITALIZATION:

1. several of his jewish relatives traveled to jerusalem for passover*.

* a religious event

PUNCTUATION:

2. One fifth of the class must bring the following for the craft yarn pine cones but tons and paint

PARTS OF SPEECH: NOUNS
   Write the possessive:

3. A.   pearls given to Tara - _____

   B.   problems shared by many cities - _____

   C.   an opinion expressed by two women - _____

DICTIONARY SKILLS: ALPHABETIZING
   Write these words in alphabetical order:

4. pride   pardon   quiet   prim   quake   pristine

ANALOGIES:
   Circle the correct answer:

5. wave : gesture :: tag : _____
    (a) price   (b) clothing   (c) label   (d) knot

SENTENCE COMBINING:

6. Mt. Vesuvius is a volcano on the Bay of Naples.
    Mt. Vesuvius erupted in 79 A.D.
    It destroyed Pompeii, Italy.

_____

_____

DAY 170

CAPITALIZATION:

1.   a greek student read about richard I in a british history class.

PUNCTUATION:
   Write the abbreviation:

2.   A.   kilometer - _____   B.   pound - _____   C.   ounce - _____

SUBJECT/VERB:
   **With either/or and neither/nor, make the verb agree with
   the subject after or or nor.**

   Example: Neither <u>Micah</u> *nor* his <u>sisters</u> (<u>like</u>, likes) spinach.

   Underline the subject once; underline the verb twice:

3.   Either his grandparents or his father (volunteer, volunteers) at that shelter.

PARTS OF SPEECH: NOUNS

4.   An example of an abstract noun is _____.

ANALOGIES:
   Circle the correct answer:

5.   emancipate : free :: mutiny : _____
     (a) mutter   (b) assist   (c) muzzle   (d) rebel

SENTENCE COMBINING:

6.   Dad makes pickled eggs.
     He cooks the eggs.
     He peels the cooled eggs.
     He places the eggs in beet juice.

   _____

   _____

CAPITALIZATION:
   Capitalize these titles:

1.   A.   "a big mistake"
     B.   "a look into the future"
     C.   much ado about nothing

PUNCTUATION:

2.   Tina said Youve heard of course that hes moving

PARTS OF SPEECH: VERBS
   Underline the subject once and the verb phrase twice:

3.   A.   Kim could have (came, come) earlier to help.
     B.   A balloon has (bursted, burst).
     C.   I should have (knew, known) the answer.
     D.   Has Josh (beaten, beat) your record?
     E.   The new juror has been (sworn, swore) in.

PHRASES/CLAUSES:
   Write P if words form a phrase; write C if the words form a clause:

4.   A. _____ Having gone to the market.   B. _____ The fall craft show was a success.

SPELLING:
   Write the correct spelling of these words:

5.   A.   disgrace + ful - _____   C.   deny + al - _____
     B.   recur + ing - _____   D.   strap + ed - _____

SENTENCE COMBINING:

6.   The leather saddle was invented 2,000 years ago.
     It was invented by Asian warriors.

     _____

     _____

DAY 172

CAPITALIZATION:

1. samuel champlain, a frenchman, was the founder of fort quebec in canada.

PUNCTUATION:

2.   12507 N 67th St
                                      Scottsdale AZ 85254
                                      June 1 20--
        Dear Mano
              We arrived at two oclock last Thursday May 7   Lets
        meet next week at my aunts house on Elkton Ridge
                                      Always
                                      Lanzo

DICTIONARY SKILLS: GUIDE WORDS
    Place a √ if the word will appear on a page with the guide words:
                            freight - fresh:

3. A. ___ frequent   B. ___ freezer   C. ___ French   D. ___ fretwork

PARTS OF SPEECH: ADVERBS
    Circle the correct adverb:

4. The detective examined the sixth piece of evidence (more closely, most closely).

ANALOGIES:
    Circle the correct answer:

5. rejoicing : mourning :: split : _____
    (a) regain   (b) banana   (c) sever   (d) fuse

SENTENCE COMBINING:

6. Silver balls hang on a Christmas tree.
    The tree is gigantic.
    The tree is in a department store.

    _____

    _____

CAPITALIZATION:

1. is triangle x ranch located in grand teton national park of jackson, wyoming?

PUNCTUATION:

2. Yes those ladies holiday plans most definitely must be considered

PREFIXES/ROOTS/SUFFIXES:
    Ologist **is a suffix that means an expert in a specific study.**
    Card **is a root that relates to the heart.**
    Using this information, explain the word, *cardiologist.*

3. _____

PARTS OF SPEECH: NOUNS
    Write the plural:

4. A. child - _____   E. centipede - _____

    B. cliff - _____   F. sheep - _____

    C. trophy - _____   G. mystery - _____

    D. pitch - _____   H. atlas - _____

ANALOGIES:
    Circle the correct answer:

5. swarm : bees :: drove : _____
    (a) swans   (b) doves   (c) turkeys   (d) cattle

SENTENCE COMBINING:

6. Ten cheerleaders ran onto the football field.
    The cheerleaders waved their pompoms.
    The team ran behind them.

    _____

    _____

DAY 174

CAPITALIZATION:

1.   are the hausa people who live in nigeria of the islamic faith?

PUNCTUATION:
   Place a dash (the width of <u>M</u>) or parentheses ( ) to provide additional information.

        Example: The photographer told us to stand still – perfectly still.

                     The photographer told us to stand still **(perfectly still).**

2.   Our Mexican food was hot   extremely hot

PARTS OF SPEECH: NOUNS
   Place a √ by the correct possessive form:

3.   A. ____ writers' conference   B. ____ mens' club
       ____ writer's conference   ____ men's club

FRIENDLY LETTER ENVELOPES:
   Write your return address. Address the envelope to Lou Mariana who lives in Honolulu, Hawaii. The street address is 2 Moanalua Freeway. The zip code is 96819.

4.   _____

      _____
      _____
      _____

                              _____
                              _____
                              _____

      _____

SPELLING:
   Circle the correct spelling:

5.   A.   amusment   amusement
     B.   writen   written
     C.   applied   applyed

SENTENCE COMBINING:

6.   Craig's neighbors rode in the Chunnel.
   They went from London to Paris.

CAPITALIZATION:

1. during world war I, many americans fought in europe on the allies' side.

PUNCTUATION:

2. Their television was too loud too loud for me

PARTS OF SPEECH: ADVERBS/ADJECTIVES
Circle the correct answer:

3. A. Their father lay down because he didn't feel (well, good).

   B. Is this a (real, really) scary movie?

SENTENCE TYPES:
Place end punctuation; write the sentence type:

4. A. Yes! You did it   _____

   B. May I have a glass of lemonade   _____

   C. She insisted on washing the dog herself   _____

   D. Tell me about your new fish   _____

ANALOGIES:
Circle the correct answer:

5. company : employee :: congregation : _____
   (a) church   (b) gathering   (c) person   (d) hymnal

SENTENCE COMBINING:

6. Thomas Kuykendall is an artist.
   He is famous for his duck carvings.
   He begins each duck with a block of wood.

   _____

   _____

DAY 176

CAPITALIZATION:

1. located in northeast tanzania, mt. kilimanjaro is the highest peak in africa.

PUNCTUATION:

2. I think   said Debra that Hampton Virginia was started by Jamestown colonists

SYNONYMS/ANTONYMS/HOMONYMS:
Circle the antonym for *optional*:

3. optional: (a) voluntary   (b) elective   (c) compulsory   (d) unforced

FRIENDLY LETTERS/ENVELOPES:

4. The two lines that are the same in a heading of a friendly letter and in a return address of an envelope are the _____ and

   _____.

ANALOGIES:
Circle the correct answer:

5. lethal : deadly :: effervescent : _____
   (a) efficient   (b) effective   (c) fluid   (d) bubbly

SENTENCE COMBINING:

6. Jackson is a cat.
   He belongs to Parker.
   Jackson weighs over twenty pounds.
   Jackson has a gentle disposition.

   _____

   _____

CAPITALIZATION:

1. he always reads "the midnight ride of paul revere" on independence day.

PUNCTUATION:

2. This recipe I believe calls for self rising flour   said Sharon

PARTS OF SPEECH: NOUNS
   Circle any nouns:

3. Bonnie and I have little patience for gossip and other negative comments.

PREFIXES/ROOTS/SUFFIXES
   de, ab, dis - away from
   co, com - together
   sub - under, below
   Using the meaning of the prefix, explain each word:

4. A. absent - _____

   B. subzero - _____

   C. cooperate - _____

SPELLING:
   Write the correct spelling of the word:

5. A. precise + ion - _____

   B. rally + ed - _____

   C. expel + ed - _____

   D. rally + ing - _____

SENTENCE COMBINING:

6. Wessex is a former Anglo-Saxon kingdom.
   It is in Great Britain.
   It is the setting for Thomas Hardy's novels.

   _____

   _____

DAY 178

CAPITALIZATION:

Capitalize these lines of poetry by William Wordsworth:

1. the world is too much with us, late and soon,

    getting and spending, we lay waste our powers:

PUNCTUATION:

2. That picture said Tate was done by Norman Rockwell a famous American artist

PARTS OF SPEECH: VERBS

Underline the subject once and the verb phrase twice:

3.   A.   The waiter had (brang, brought) water with lemon.

     B.   Mom has (went, gone) out to repair our fence.

     C.   The child was (sitting, setting) on a rocking horse.

     D.   Have you ever (drank, drunk) raspberry tea?

     E.   I must have (ran, run) out of time.

PARTS OF SPEECH: ADJECTIVES

Circle the correct adjective:

4.   Their second guess was (more reasonable, most reasonable) than their first.

ANALOGIES:

Circle the correct answer:

5.   exact : precise :: rich : _____

     (a) fertile   (b) poor   (c) precarious   (d) futile

SENTENCE COMBINING:

6.   The Volkswagen Beetle was built in the 1930's.
     It was built in Germany.
     The designer was Dr. Ferdinand Porsche.

     _____

     _____

CAPITALIZATION:

1. "this victorian needlepoint," said alicia, "is that of mary, queen of scots."

PUNCTUATION:
Use underlining or quotation marks:

2. A. a movie, Poor Little Rich Girl
   B. a plane, Hawk Hunter
   C. an essay, Comparing Haiku with Other Poetry

PARTS OF SPEECH: PRONOUNS
Circle the correct pronoun:

3. The mayor handed Allie and (me, I) our awards.

PARTS OF SPEECH: VERBS
Write a sentence using the future tense:

4. _____

   _____

SIMPLE/COMPOUND SENTENCES:
Write a compound sentence:

5. _____

   _____

SENTENCE COMBINING:

6. She once had frostbite on her toes.
   Her toes become cold quickly.

   _____

   _____

DAY 180

CAPITALIZATION:

1. on labor day, our family will stay in an orlando hotel and visit the regency center.

PUNCTUATION:

2. A mens reading group is forming its first meeting will be next Thursday June 1

PARTS OF SPEECH: NOUNS

Underline the subject once and the verb or verb phrase twice.   Label the direct object - D.O. and the indirect object - I.O.:

3. That vitamin company has sent my parents herbal tablets.

SENTENCES/FRAGMENTS/RUN-ONS:

Write S for sentence, F for fragment, and R-O for run-on:

4. A. _____   Holly cut lettuce from her garden.

B. _____   Drew bought a 1950's jukebox it was too large to go through the door.

C. _____   Art and history rolled into one.

ANALOGIES:

Circle the correct answer:

5. coat : parka :: cloud : _____
   (a) stratus   (b) atmosphere   (c) sky   (d) space

SENTENCE COMBINING:

6. Amphibians have lungs.
   Amphibians are cold-blooded.
   Amphibians have moist skin.
   The skin is hairless.

   _____

   _____